MW00612066

THE FAN BOOK

Text prepared and book designed
by Robert Scharff and Associates, Ltd.
New Ringgold, Pennsylvania

RESTON PUBLISHING COMPANY, INC.
A Prentice-Hall Company
Reston, Virginia

CONTENTS

ISBN 0-8359-1855-6

Reston Publishing Company, Inc.
A Prentice-Hall Company
Reston, Virginia 22090

10 9 8 7 6 5 4 3 2

Printed in the United States of America

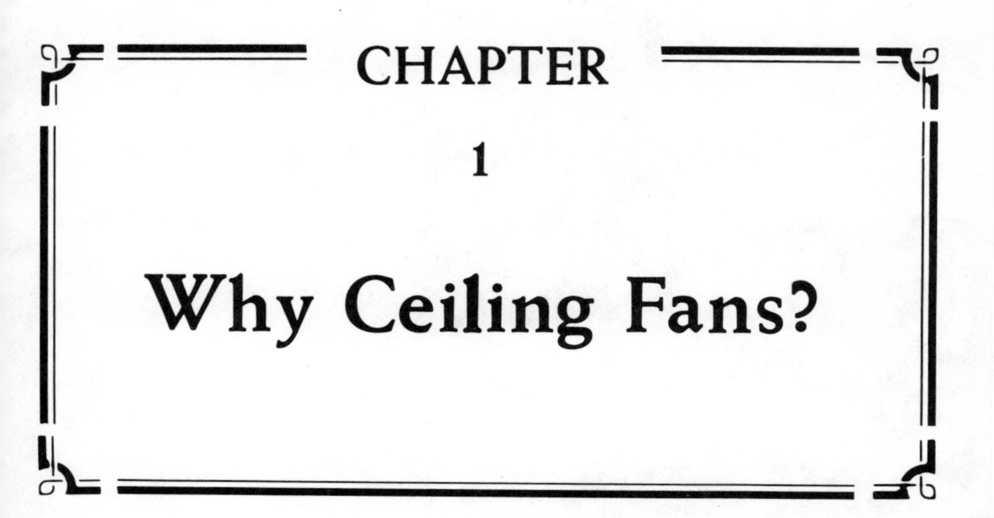

CHAPTER 1

Why Ceiling Fans?

Few if any items found in the home can match a ceiling fan's combination of outward beauty (Figure 1-1), functional effectiveness, and long term dependability. A quality ceiling fan increases the beauty and value of any home or apartment. It can also lower heating and cooling costs, a fact which makes a ceiling fan an investment that pays for itself.

Ceiling fans make air behave, and a properly directed and maintained airflow can have either a cooling or warming effect. Everyone has experienced the cooling effects of a light breeze. As air moves across the skin it evaporates body moisture, making one feel cooler and more comfortable. With a ceiling fan generating cooling breezes in your home, you can set your air conditioning thermostat at a higher, more economical level. You save money without sacrificing comfort.

Yet a ceiling fan is more than a cooling device (Figure 1-2). It can also be used to more effectively distribute heat throughout your home. Because warm air rises, cool air can become trapped near floor level. This stratification of air layers can be a problem during colder months, especially in rooms with high or domed ceilings. A ceiling fan breaks up these cool and warm layers, making the overall room temperature more uniform. By simply flipping a switch to reverse the fan's normal airflow, warm air is moved across the ceiling and down the walls. This helps distribute room heat without creating a cooling draft. The result is a room that is warm where you need it—at the level you live in, not near the ceiling. So, in winter you can lower your furnace thermostat several degrees, again saving energy dollars. Ceiling fans can also help guarantee proper airflow in solar and other alternative fuel heating systems. The noiseless operation and variable running speeds of

Figure 1-1: Ceiling fans combine beauty and functional effectiveness.

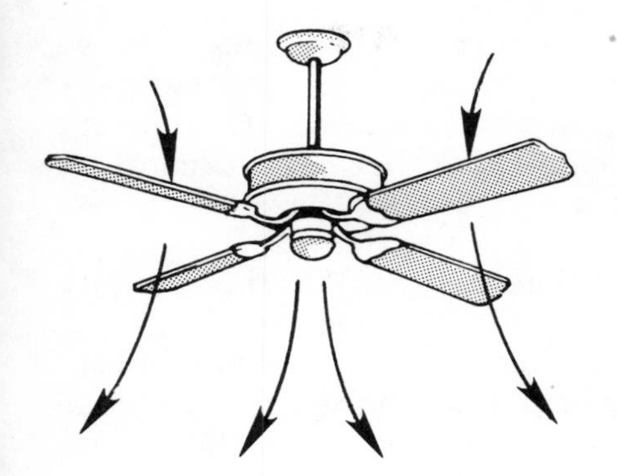

Figure 1-2: A ceiling fan can force cool air downward in the summer (left) as well as circulate warm air in the winter (below).

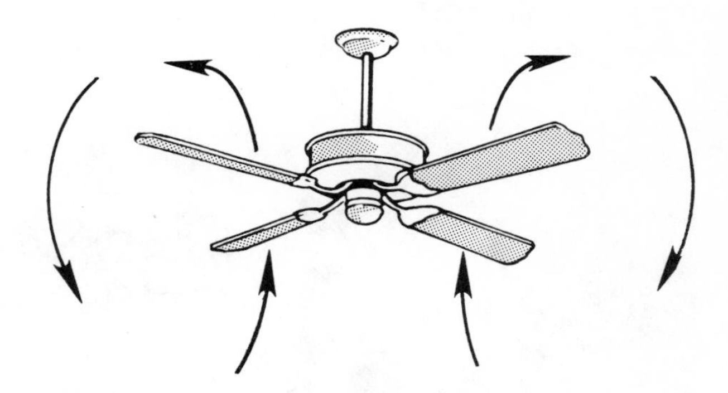

quality fans allow their use in virtually any room of the home, day or night. And all this is possible with a fan that draws less electricity than a 100-watt light bulb.

What's more, a ceiling fan, unlike other decorative efforts, is a movable investment. Those who live in apartments can still enjoy the comfort, elegance, and energy saving benefits that a ceiling fan provides without the worry of losing their investment should they decide to move. Unlike wallpaper and most floor coverings, which must be left behind and are big investments with little return, the ceiling fan is a decorating touch that can be packed right along with the boxes and furniture when the next moving day comes—an investment with a big return.

Ceiling fans can solve other problems, too. For instance, while searching for unique gift ideas, every so often we all get lucky and find just the right item for that "special" person. Available in a wide range of styles and colors, ceiling fans can be a most unique idea that is also practical, an important consideration in today's world. A ceiling fan would be a great gift for the kids on their way to college for their dorm rooms where temperatures are frequently uneven and uncontrollable.

Mom would love one for the kitchen or porch (Figure 1-3). Dad could use a ceiling fan in his workshop where the air may be damp or stuffy. A ceiling fan is also ideal for a den or the family's game room (Figure 1-4). Newly married couples would appreciate a gift that meets decorating and energy-saving needs. What better way to say, "I'm your biggest fan."

Most fans can be easily installed by the purchaser. This is especially true of quality lightweight fans. These lighter fans can be safely hung from metal electrical junction boxes already firmly secured in the ceiling. Of course, appearance can only be judged by the consumer. The wide varieties of blade styles, accessory light fixtures, finishes, and trim make it possible to custom design a fan to fit any decor. Not to be repetitive, but a ceiling fan is one of the simplest and most effective ways of creating a distinct atmosphere in any room of your home. The

Figure 1-3: Ceiling fans can be used on a porch or patio just as long as they are carefully located.

Figure 1-4: A recreation room is a good place for a ceiling fan.

pleasing aesthetic appearance of quality workmanship, the silent, tranquilizing rhythm of motion, and the economic benefits in heating and cooling make the ceiling fan one of the world's most useful appliances.

It may seem odd to call a ceiling fan an appliance. It doesn't make toast, spin a soufflé, sew a dress, or cook. But by definition, an appliance is an instrument, apparatus, or device for a particular use. The definition fits. The ceiling fan enhances our environment and adds to our comfort. It meets a need. In fact, the ceiling fan was the very first electric device to do so, for it was the original electrical appliance. The electric toaster, blender, sewing machine, and range wouldn't be here today if the way had not been led by the discovery of electricity, the search for useful applications of this new form of energy, and the clever Americans who invented the first practical device that put electricity to work—the ceiling fan.

CEILING FANS—A PROUD HISTORY

Personal cooling devices have been around ever since some overheated anthropoid discovered that waving a palm leaf in front of his face produced the agreeable sensation of a refreshing breeze. This historical first "wind chill" was duplicated by the royalty and wealthy persons of early Assyria and Egypt who employed a small army of slaves and servants waving huge leaves to make them feel cool on hot days.

Hand fans, still seen today, came into being around the birth of Christ. The *Akomeogi*, the Japanese folding fan, dates back to sixth century, A.D. A century or so later, the popular Chinese dancing fan, *Mai Ogi*, appeared with its ten sticks and a thick paper mount depicting the family crest. In India, a large fan of peacock feathers symbolized the eternal vigilance of the ruler.

The hand fan was introduced to Europeans in the Middle Ages and soon became popular. By the mid 1750s in Paris alone, there were 150 master fan makers. At about this time, the world's great inventors started to grapple with the problem of designing mechanically powered, personal wind-generating machines (Figure 1-5). Some of the more successful of these machines that have appeared at various times in the *Smithsonian*—the official magazine of the Smithsonian Institute in Washington, D.C.—are shown in Figures 1-6 to 1-10.

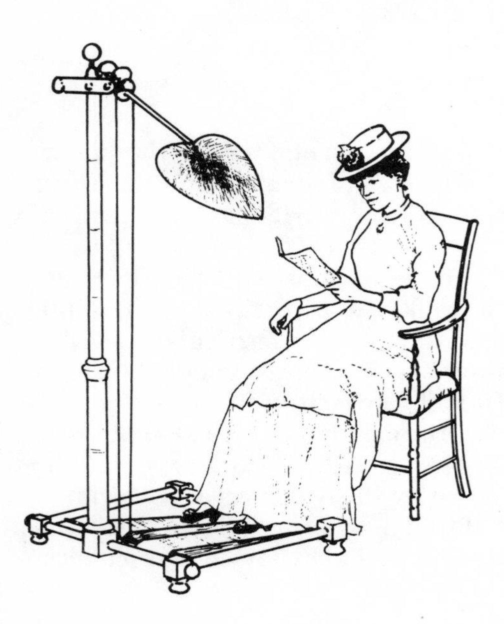

Figure 1-5: The treadle-operated fan used foot power to produce a zephyr, leaving hands free.

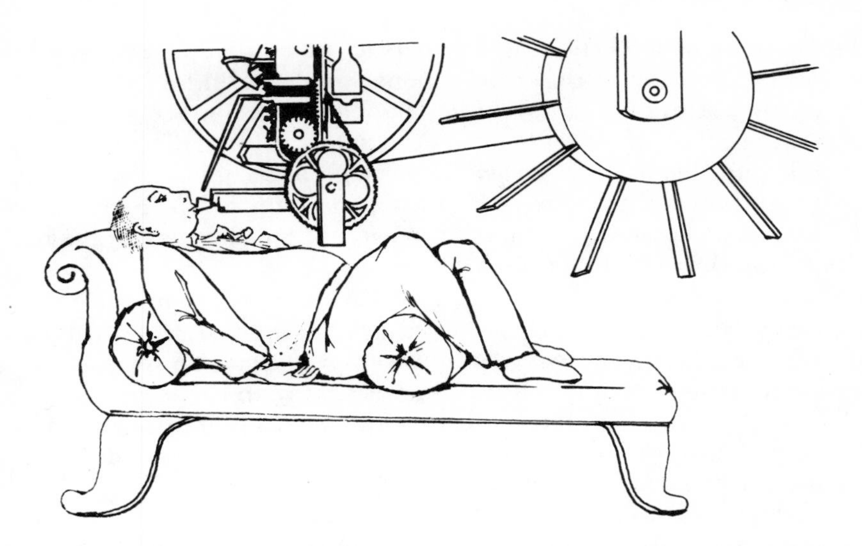

Figure 1-6: Summer's ease, as depicted in a 19th-century British caricature, is produced by a mechanical contraption that fans the body, cracks nuts, and serves wine, too.

An early and successful use of mechanical fans was developed in the steamy factories of the Industrial Revolution. Workers sweating at their tasks got the idea of attaching wooden or metal blades to the whirling line shafts overhead that were used to drive the machinery. The resulting breeze was evidently so satisfying that within a few years most factories on a hot summer day were in danger of having their roofs fly away as long rows of line-shaft fans howled over the workers' heads.

Thomas Jefferson, a toiler more at home in the vineyards than the sweatshops, nevertheless cared enough about the comfort of his dinner guests during the sweltering summers in Virginia to take a crack at designing a mechanical fan that would propel the air above his table at Monticello. As in almost everything he did, Jefferson recorded his thoughts about mechanical fans in a notebook, including a full analysis of the operation of the device.

He begins with a description of the area above his dining room table, where "a pendulum is to be fixed, with its claws to catch into what is called the swing wheel of a clock, or rather a barrel wheel with the teeth of a swing wheel. A cord round the barrel of the swing wheel, carried to a pulley over the well of the stairs and having a heavy weight, will put the swing wheel into motion. The teeth of that laying hold of the claws of the pendulum will keep that in vibration, and consequently the fan wing which is tenanted into its axis exactly under the skylight, and of the breadth of the funnel mouth of the skylight."

Having got his fan properly positioned, Jefferson the physicist begins to speculate on how to make it go faster or slower. "The vibrations may be retarded or accelerated 1. by the great weight, 2. by the bob of the pendulum, 3. by the length of the pendulum rod, 4. by the size of the fan. With so many regulating powers it will be easy to make the vibrations that shall be found best."

But it was Jefferson the perfectionist who improved on his own fan design as a final thought. He proposed a way to make the fan turn faster, although at the ultimate cost of more elbow grease. "Suppose besides the swing wheel, it should have pinions taking in the teeth of a barrel wheel making one revolution for two, three or four of the swing wheel. Consequences: the weight must be proportionally increased, and consequently the exertion in winding up."

Jefferson's dining room fan, if it was ever built (and there is no physical evidence at Monticello that it ever was), probably would have been used much like his famous hall clock, whose cannonball-like weights marked the days of the week. Imagine the anxiety of a guest who, looking at the inexorable drop of the weight down the stairwell, realizes to his horror that he is still working on the meat course when the heavy ball is registering dessert.

One might speculate that the obvious difficulty in bringing a line-shaft system into the home sent aspiring inventors of mechanical personal cooling machines into a frenzy of creativity; undoubtedly, they hoped to profit from an invention they knew was likely to be a money-maker.

James Barron thought he had the answer in 1830 when he patented a fan with a clockwork power unit that could be carried from room to room. The fan proper, however, had to be firmly attached to the ceiling, which meant that the purchaser of the Barron system was required to modify a number of rooms in order to be cooled in the place he wanted to sit or lie down. Apparently recognizing this as economically unsound, Barron returned to the Patent Office the following year with a revised design that incorporated the fan and its power unit in one heavy—but movable—package.

A rendering of Barron's first fan design was prepared by Charles Lewis Fleischmann, a draftsman employed by the United States Commissioner of Patents to reproduce some of the 16,000 models and drawings lost in the calamitous Patent Office fire of 1836. Fleischmann seemed to poke sly fun at the inventor in this drawing, suggesting that perhaps the work involved in winding the apparatus and hauling it from room to room would so exhaust the user that he would sleep through the cooling cycle. He showed a man slumbering on a lovely Greek revival couch, an unlighted pipe slipping from his hands, and a newspaper at his side that called itself the *Hardworking Men Journal.* The paper's headline read "Hard Times."

One or two inventors approached the matter of personal "air conditioners" with greater precision, realizing that the effort required to cool the whole body was substantially greater than cooling just those human parts that invariably got the hottest. Daniel Linzie of Petersham, Massachusetts, designed a device (Figure 1-7) in 1849 that went right to the heart of the problem. His rocking-chair operated bellows was connected to movable tubes that could aim jets of air at wrists, armpits, and neck, precisely those points where arterial flow is nearest the surface of the skin. Later, in 1869, another jet rocker, designed by Charles Singer of South Bend, Indiana, was patented that blasted air from a carved snake (Figure 1-8) positioned just above the head of the chair's occupant. While this curious cooler operated on the same principle as the Linzie rocker, its effectiveness was probably due as much to sheer terror as to moisture evaporation.

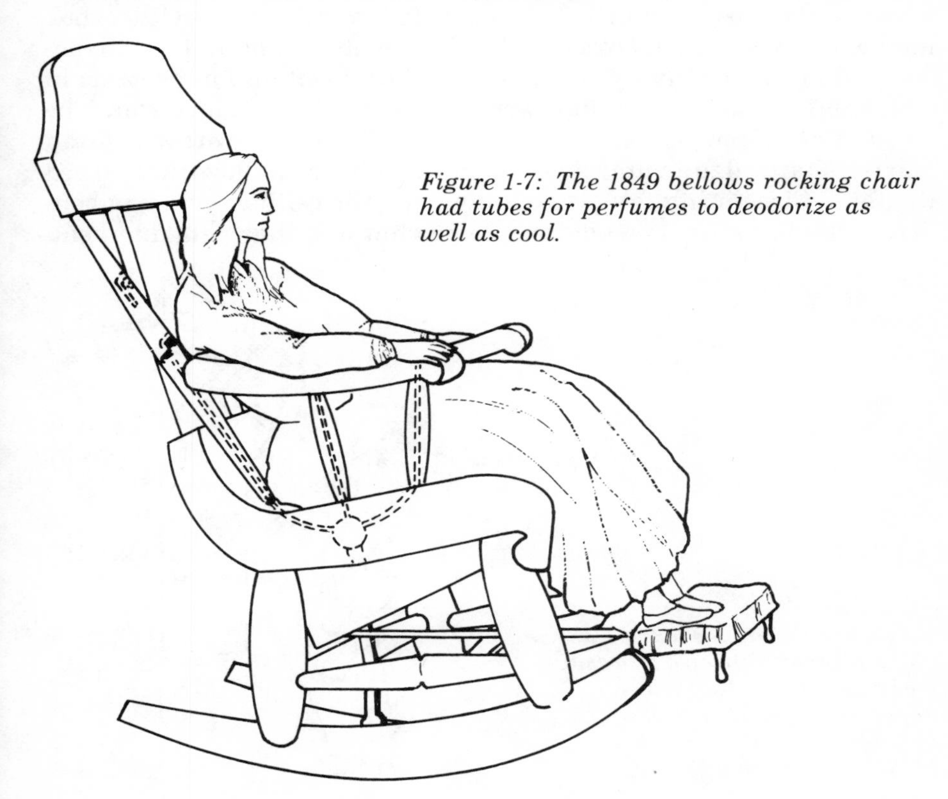

Figure 1-7: The 1849 bellows rocking chair had tubes for perfumes to deodorize as well as cool.

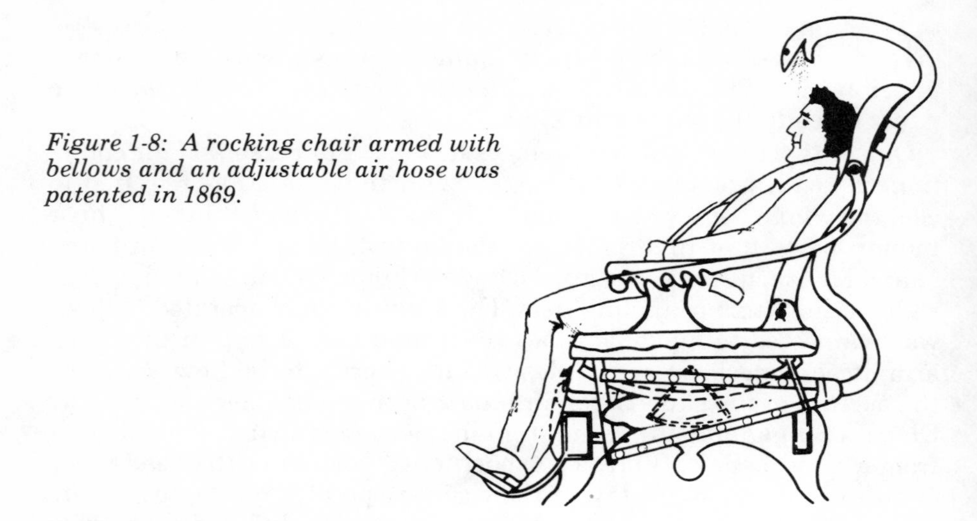

Figure 1-8: A rocking chair armed with bellows and an adjustable air hose was patented in 1869.

During this period of history, other forms of mechanically driven fans also gained a certain degree of popularity (Figure 1-9). Other cooling devices were run by clockwork-driven motors (Figure 1-10), treadles, and most cleverly by water power. Whole ceiling fan systems in stores, offices, and dwellings were powered by running water. The steady flow of a water jet turned a turbine. The turbine drove a shaft, and the shaft led to an amazing maze of belt-driven pulleys that turned the fans. Circulating fans were hung from the ceiling, with the belt-drives flip-flapping a steady and somewhat less than relaxing beat.

Figure 1-9: In an age when a shave and a haircut were also five cents, a cartoonist spoofed the new popularity of electric fans with a curbside-breeze-for-a-nickel kiosk model.

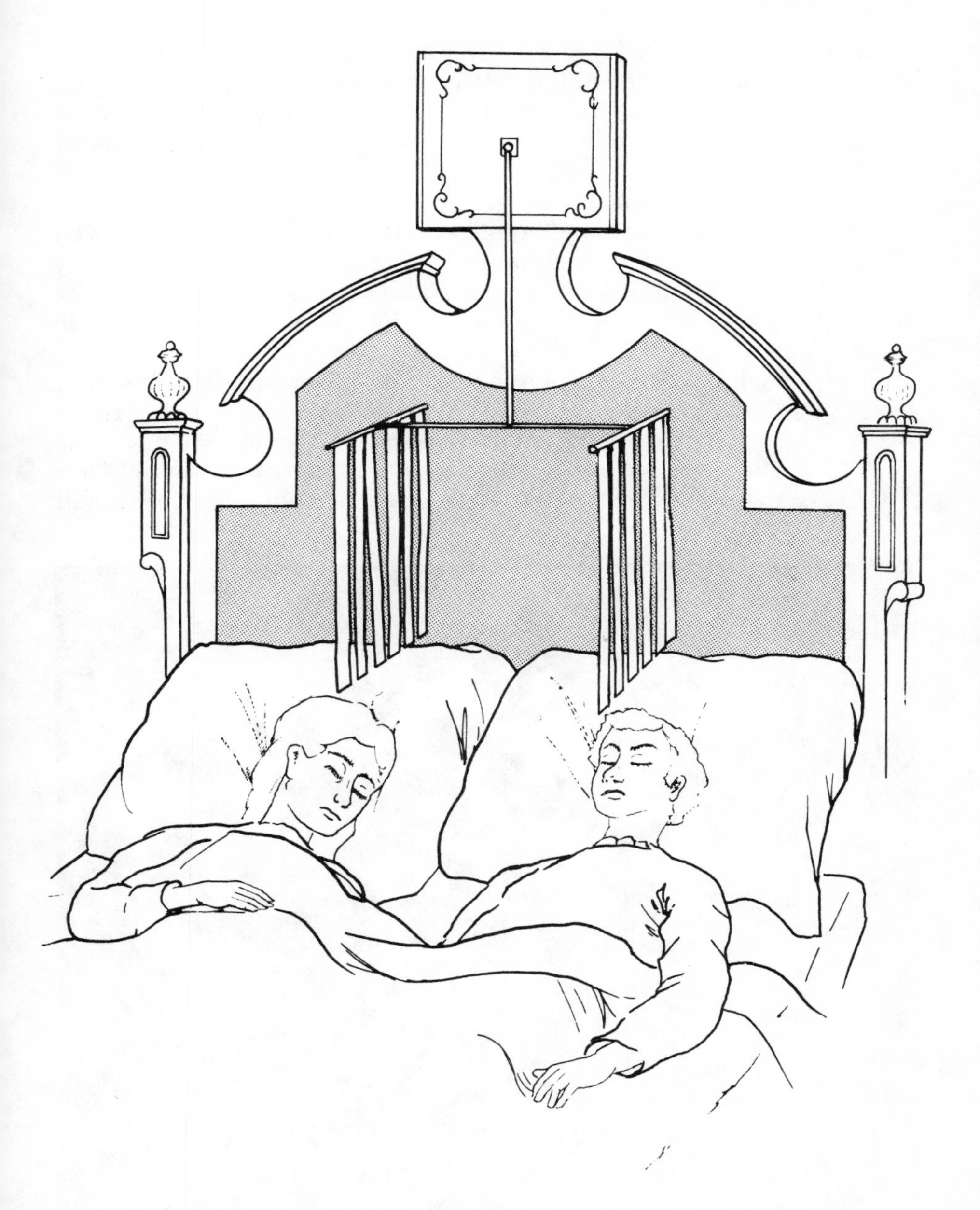

Figure 1-10: A clockwork-driven fan was designed to cool sleepers and drive away insects. The mechanism was to run for 6-1/2 hours, providing a cool night's sleep. But, it was a far cry from the beauty and comfort of modern ceiling fans.

Other systems had the large, flat circular fans mounted on posts coming up from the floor or counter, with the belt-drives hidden below. By the 1870s this form of ceiling or floor-based fan was a standard fixture in restaurants, confectionaries, and hotels. Many of the "old" systems are still in use (Figure 1-11).

The sheer size of the mechanical apparatus necessary to drive these fan systems often limited their applications. However, one man was on the verge of a discovery which would revolutionize the American way of life. In 1882, Thomas Edison introduced the first viable system for the large scale use of electrical power. The ceiling fan was about to come of age.

Electricity had been considered as a fan power source before that time. But electricity was little more than a parlor game when Louis Stein of New York filed a patent on December 19, 1854 for a device he called an "Improvement in Revolving Fans for Apartments." New York City was in its boom and growth years following the opening of

Figure 1-11: A typical paddlewheel fan system.

the Erie Canal, with tightly packed apartments rapidly replacing the single family dwellings of the past. Keeping people comfortable became a real need. Stein provided a brilliant solution with a ceiling mounted device that would, in the language of his patent, "agitate the air in the apartment by a revolving and flapping motion by means of wings...hinged along one edge to the horizontal arms projecting from a hollow shaft." The most significant part of his invention was its power, described as "rotary motion...imparted by electro-magnets connected with a suitable galvanic battery." It was the first time electricity had been applied to do something really useful. The ceiling fan had become America's first electrical appliance. But, the idea of an electric ceiling fan wasn't practical at that time. The problem was the wet cell batteries. They were inefficient and ran out of power faster than a modern flashlight battery.

Edison's commercially practical system for the manufacture and transmission of electricity eliminated the need for short-lived, ineffective wet cell batteries. Inexpensive power coupled with the development of simple, efficient electric motors paved the way for a ceiling fan boom.

Philip Diehl is generally considered the father of the modern electric ceiling fan. One of the giants of the electrical industry, Diehl was the inventive genius and head of Messrs. Diehl and Company of Elizabeth, New Jersey. One of Diehl's greatest projects, and one which eventually led to the development of the ceiling fan, was the engineering of an electric motor suitable for use in Singer sewing machines. While this motor was flat and considerably larger than the sewing machine motor of today, it gained immediate acceptance on the heavy commercial sewing machines that fostered the ready-to-wear garment industry. Diehl's success as a component supplier led his interest to the creation of a proprietary product of his own. In 1882, with great fanfare, Diehl announced his "invention of the electric ceiling fan." His device was a large double-blade adaptation of the well-known belt driven fan with its own self-contained electric motor; the latter, a modification of his sewing machine motor. By the end of the 1880s, "The Diehl Electric Fan" was sweeping the country.

At this same time the introduction of electric lights, electric street car railways, and dozens of home electrical appliances was bringing the wonders of electricity to cities and towns across the country. The construction of hundreds of generators and transmission stations made electrical power inexpensive and readily available. Inventors and imitators scrambled to make their fortunes.

The idea of interior environmental control caught on like wildfire, giving Diehl immediate competition. Soon there were half a dozen electric ceiling fan producers, then a dozen or more. An endless variety of the appliances were produced in designs noted for their elegance, trim, and beauty. Philip Diehl continued to make major improvements and innovations, such as reducing motor size and adding lights to create the Diehl "Electrolier," or electrified combination chandelier and ceiling fan, the ultimate development in ceiling fan usefulness and beauty. Soon the idea also became common property, and by the turn of the century the ceiling fan was everywhere. It wasn't long before its fame, and sales, had traveled around the world.

By World War I, most ceiling fans were being made with four blades to maximize the cooling and heating efficiency of their motors. By the late 1920s, no self-respecting restaurant, drug store, ice cream parlor, elegant dining room, or even "speakeasy" was without a bank of ceiling fans as part of their decor and ventilating system (Figure 1-12). Many styles of ceiling fans made their appearances during this time (Figure 1-13).

Figure 1-12: In the early 1900s, ceiling fans were part of many cooling schemes.

Figure 1-13: Many different style fans made their appearance in the 1920s.

Ironically, the same inexpensive power that made the widespread use of electric ceiling fans possible also led to their downfall. Despite its economic turmoil, the America entering the grim depression of the 1930s was an abundantly energy-rich society. Technical advances of the day reflected this abundance. Air conditioning and central forced air heating were two perfect examples. It mattered little to both manufacturers and consumers that these cooling and heating innovations consumed enormous amounts of energy. Energy was inexpensive, the future was at hand, and having survived the most devastating decade of its history, America was ready for a change.

In its rush to forget the past, America forgot the ceiling fan. One by one, as they wore out or as establishments redecorated, the old ceiling fans were discarded and replaced with energy demanding cooling and heating units. By the end of World War II and into the 1950s, the reliable and economical ceiling fan of the recent past had become almost extinct. Those that remained were considered curiosity pieces or nostalgic reminders of the past. In fact, many of our younger generation never saw ceiling fans except in TV reruns of the Humphrey Bogart classic, *Casablanca.*

Burton A. Burton, founder of the CasaBlanca Fan Company, developed his interest in ceiling fans in 1973, with an observation of a ceiling fan cooling a New Orleans restaurant. That belt-driven fan (Figure 1-14) inspired an entrepreneurial idea: Ceiling fans could be improved upon and, very likely, there would be a considerable market for them. So working from the premise that these highly practical and decorative fans would be very popular among restaurant owners throughout the world, Burton enthusiastically went to work. Drawing on his experience in engineering and precision machinery fabrication, Burton designed and created the company's first ceiling fan (Figure 1-15).

In 1974, the new CasaBlanca Fan Company opened an attractive display at the National Restaurant Association Convention in Chicago and almost immediately was doing a brisk business selling belt-driven fans to restaurants worldwide. Those very first CasaBlanca ceiling fans are still cooling dining rooms throughout the United States and in many nations around the globe. In fact, they were such a success that CasaBlanca soon expanded its product line. With his staff, Burton methodically took apart other self-contained ceiling fan motors, studied the components, and began redesigning them to be more efficient. And the timing couldn't have been better. The country was suffering under the longest heat wave of the decade. Simultaneously, spiraling energy costs were sending utility bills to all-time highs. People were ready for a fresh idea in cost-efficient cooling.

Figure 1-14: Belt-driven fans were popular in the 1870s in New Orleans.

Figure 1-15: CasaBlanca ceiling fan number 1.

Burton realized that a ceiling fan could actually pay for itself in as little as three years by doing the same job in today's homes that it did during the introduction of the fan in the early 1900s. The ceiling fan is an energy-efficient way to reduce electric bills because it moves air across the human body, causing a cooling effect and lowering body temperature. Consumers agreed. The total sales of ceiling fans in this country have soared to more than 6 million per year. The old-fashioned ceiling fan is back, with five times more being sold than three years ago.

In 1981, to commemorate the 100th anniversary of the ceiling fan, the CasaBlanca Fan Company offered a fan that captured the spirit of 100 years of Philip Diehl's invention (Figure 1-16). We think Philip Diehl would be pleased with the Centennial fan.

Figure 1-16: The magnificent CasaBlanca Centennial fan was built to commemorate the 100th anniversary of the ceiling fan. Beautiful cast bronze and copper housed the latest in fan technology. Etched rosewood blades circled silently above hand-cut crystal light shades. Signed and numbered, only five thousand were produced and they sold for $2,000.

CHAPTER

2

Ceiling Fans for Comfort and Energy Savings

Energy conservation has become a way of life in America. Since the first major energy crunch in the mid-1970s, Americans have come to realize that wasting energy is wasting money. Yet not all suggested energy saving methods are practical, and some just do not work. True energy conservation is not found in a series of quick cure tips, such as flipping off an occasional light switch or making sure the refrigerator door is tightly sealed. Often these practices save so little money they are not worth the effort it takes to perform them.

Homeowners interested in saving substantial amounts of energy and money should consider energy conservation **investments.** Dependent upon climate and the type of energy used to heat and cool a home, a viable combination of energy conservation investments can result in substantial, long-term net savings.

The finest investments result in no loss of personal comfort, and they actually increase the value of a home. Proper insulation in walls and ceilings, caulking of cracks and seams, and weather stripping for doors and windows are excellent examples of practical energy-conscious home investments. Many of these ideas are covered in the Appendix.

Ceiling fans are another solid energy saving investment for the home. They also add a beauty and elegance to any setting that no other conservation method can match (Figure 2-1).

Ceiling fans can be a valuable part of any home energy conservation system. Consider the following: Three of the simplest methods of saving energy in the home involve turning down furnace thermostats in winter, using less air conditioning during warm periods, and heating and cooling only those areas in which people live and work.

Figure 2-1: No other conservation method can match a ceiling fan for beauty and elegance.

Ceiling fans help do all three without lowering your personal comfort level or creating any annoying inconveniences. They create gentle, uniform breezes which cool you in summer and help to effectively distribute warmth in winter. In addition, ceiling fans do this without generating the highly directional blasts of cool or hot air often associated with small portable fans or space heating units. Also, with a system of ceiling fans carefully positioned throughout the home, it is possible to create heating or cooling effects only where desired by switching on one, several, or all the fans in the system. Remember that if there is a ceiling fan in only one room, circulation will be enhanced only in that room as air won't move, to any degree, by itself.

AIR MOVEMENT AND TEMPERATURE REGULATION

Healthful conditions in your home require both ventilation (the replacement of foul air with fresh air) and circulation (air movement), as well as proper heating and cooling. Air movement or air circulation, of course, has a direct effect upon the various levels of human comfort. For example, when the outdoor temperature exceeds our personal comfort level, even the slightest breeze can be pleasantly cooling. On the other hand, during extremely cold conditions, a biting wind can rob the body of valuable heat to a point where dangerous frostbite or freezing results.

The same air movement factors which dictate comfort levels in an open environment also pertain to comfort conditions in a closed environment, such as your home or apartment. The primary function of a ceiling fan is to generate air movement or circulation throughout a room or rooms for the purpose of human comfort. In order to more fully understand the relationship between ceiling fans, air movement, and human comfort, it is best to consider some of the various factors which influence human comfort. For example, body temperature, heat loss, and heat gain are factors related to the body's internal conditions, while ambient air temperature and air velocity are external environmental factors.

Body Temperature

An individual's average body temperature is determined by the heat produced by the body and the heat it loses to the environment. The human body's principal energy and heat source is the oxidation of food, while body heat is lost to the environment through physical work, evaporative heat losses (perspiring and breathing), and dry heat loss (radiation convection). Environmental factors affecting the quantity of body heat loss include:

- relative humidity
- radiant temperature
- ambient air temperature
- air velocity.

Evaporative Heat Loss and the Windchill Factor

The human body is always experiencing evaporative heat loss either through breathing, perspiring, or a combination of both. In a closed environment, this process can be regulated by the direct circulation of air over the body. Perspiration, no matter how slight, evaporates quickly, releasing the body's excess heat to the atmosphere. When a draft is applied, evaporation takes place much faster, cooling the body more rapidly. The action of a draft removing the excess heat from a body creates what is known as the windchill factor.

To many people in climate zones where cold winter temperatures are prevalent, the windchill factor is a dangerous if not deadly adversary. The windchill factor is so effective in robbing body heat that a temperature of 15°F coupled with a 20 mile per hour wind could freeze exposed areas of the body within minutes. In warmer temperatures, however, the windchill factor can be harnessed to create more comfortable living conditions by aiding the body's own cooling process. It is in this capacity that ceiling fans realize their tremendous potential.

During hot periods, a ceiling fan may be used in conjunction with air conditioning to reduce operating costs. Because of the windchill effect, the air conditioning thermostat can usually be raised 6° to 8° with no loss of personal comfort. For each degree the air conditioning thermostat is raised, a savings of 4 to 8% of air conditioning bills can be realized. The total energy savings for a year could well be up to 40% if ceiling fans are used.

Air Velocity

It's important to keep in mind that of the four environmental factors affecting the quantity of body heat loss, the only one affected by the ceiling fan is air velocity (cooling). Actually, the rate of evaporative heat loss can be regulated by altering air velocity. The cooling effect of the windchill factor is amplified by the amount of draft present. Since most ceiling fans have variable speed controls, the amount of draft in a particular room can be regulated to suit individual needs.

In a recent paper—**Preferred Air Speeds for Comfort in Warm Conditions** by Dr. Donald A. McIntyre—a typical study of the air cooling effect on human comfort levels showed:

- In ambient temperatures from about 72°F to 86°F, people found the use of an overhead fan increased comfort.
- As ambient temperatures increase from 72°F, individuals are able to maintain original comfort levels by increasing the velocity of airflow around their bodies.
- The upper limit of air temperature for comfort is about 86°F. Above this temperature, the air velocity necessary to maintain comfort produces too much disturbance.
- Males require more air movement than females to maintain their comfort levels at a given temperature.

Table 2-1 shows typical air velocity required to maintain constant human comfort levels. The air velocities shown are **average** values; various subjects tested required up to 50% more (or less) velocity to maintain their individual comfort level. However, 86°F is the upper temperature limit to maintain an individual comfort level via the cooling effect of air movement. These conclusions apply for people who are stationary, sedate, and positioned directly in the airflow path.

Table 2-1: Velocity Required for Constant Comfort

Average Air Velocity, Feet per Second (fps)	Ambient Temperature, °F				
	72	**75**	**79**	**82**	**86**
Male	—	2.3	3.4	4.3	6.1
Female	—	0.6	2.4	3.1	—

It must be remembered that the air velocity created by a ceiling fan is **not** usually uniform across the entire length of the blades. Velocities directly under the center of the fan are relatively slow at any speed, while the maximum airflow is experienced at the center of the blade. From the center of the blades to the tips, the air velocity decreases quickly (Figure 2-2). The factors which influence airflow across the blades are the shape of the blade, the speed and number of blades, and the restrictions of airflow such as fan housing or room characteristics.

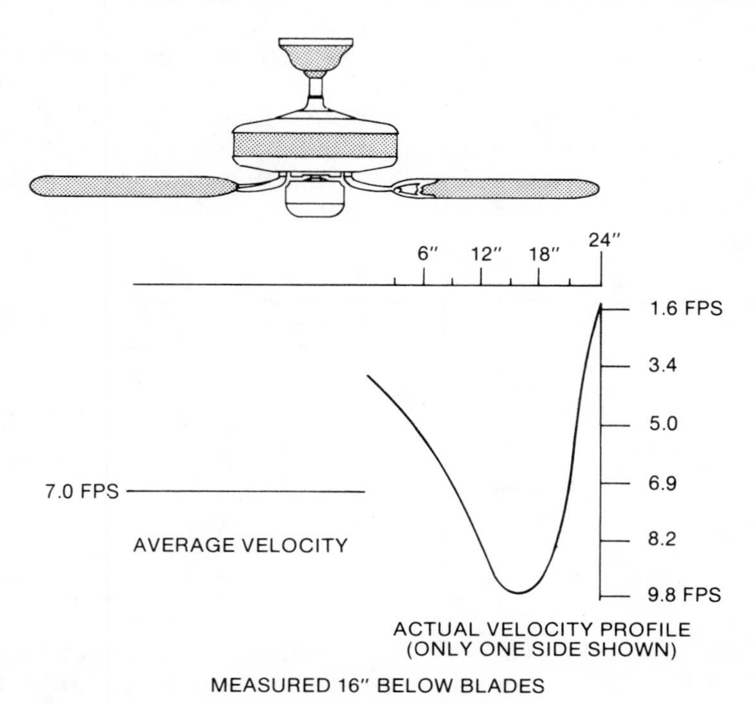

Figure 2-2: Typical ceiling fan velocity profile for a 48″ unit measured 16″ below the blades.

Air Circulation

Ceiling fans are designed primarily to circulate air in a "closed" environment. Modern-design ceiling fans are equipped with reversing switches which alter the direction of the airflow. The typical airflow patterns shown in Figures 2-3 and 2-4 indicate how the air travels around the room in downward and upward directions. The downward air over your skin has a cooling effect that is most desirable in warm weather. In cooler weather, an upward airflow recovers the wasted heat trapped at the ceiling and gently recirculates it to floor level.

AIR DESTRATIFICATION

Air will move up and down by itself. Light, warm air rises; dense, cool air falls. It won't move in any other direction unless it is assisted mechanically. Therefore, since warm air is lighter and less dense than colder air, it rises above the relatively cooler layers. In a closed space, the warmest layer of air is found at the highest point or ceiling of a room, while the coldest layer is found near the floor. In between these two layers of air, there are other temperature zones or layers (Table 2-2). In high ceiling rooms, the difference between the warmest and coldest layers can be as great as 15°F, which means that in winter, the air at a person's feet may be a cold 65°F while the air at the ceiling reaches a sweltering 80°F.

Table 2-2: Temperature Zones

Level	Height (feet)	Temperature (°F)
Floor		65°
Thermostat Height	5′	71°
Ceiling Height	8′	75°
Ceiling Height	10′	78°
Ceiling Height	12′	80°

This condition is known as air stratification, and it can be a definite problem in both winter and summer months. Ceiling fans can reclaim this wasted or misplaced heat. With the reverse switch of the fan properly set, the ceiling fan will break up stratified air layers and produce a temperature which varies as little as 2°F from the floor to the ceiling.

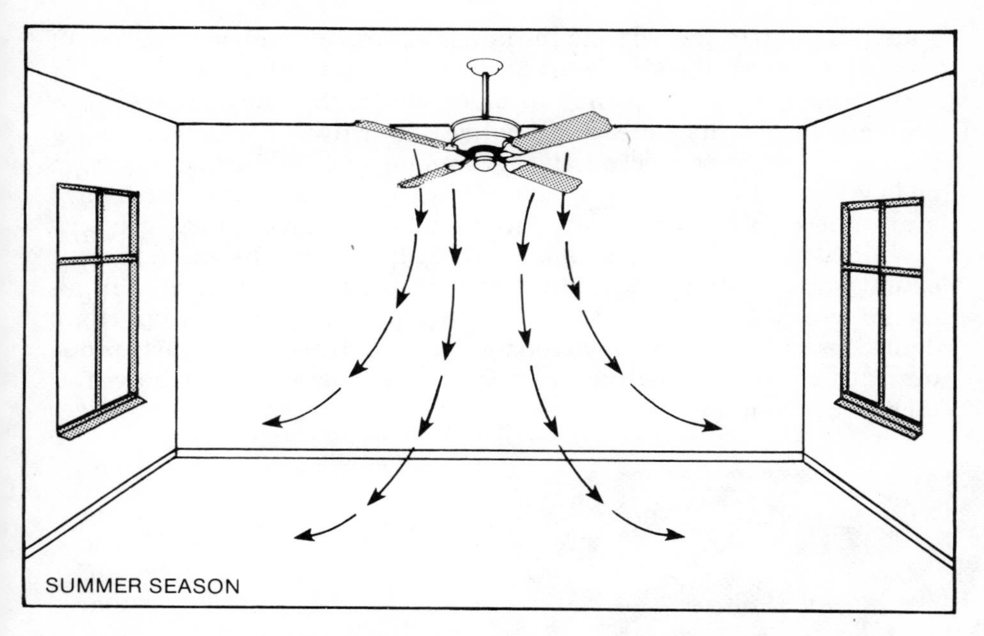

Figure 2-3: A downward draft with clockwise rotation creates a cooling breeze.

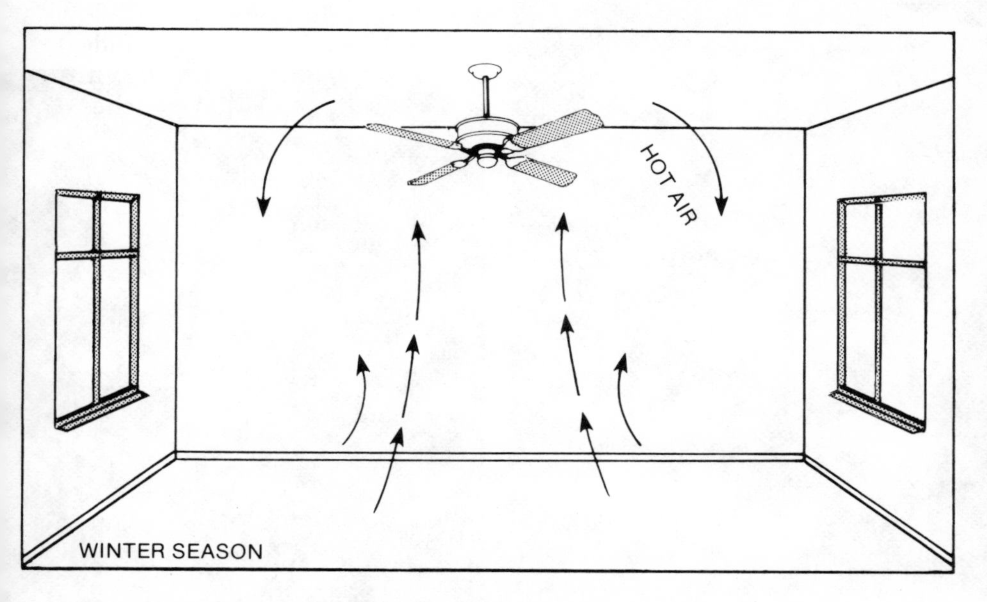

Figure 2-4: An upward draft with counterclockwise rotation recirculates warm air efficiently by eliminating hot-air stratification, without creating a direct downdraft.

As air circulates upward from the fan, the warm air is gently pushed off the ceiling, down the side walls of the room, and across the floor.

By properly adjusting the fan blade speed, this movement can be accomplished without creating a noticeable draft. When using a ceiling fan to prevent stratification, it is recommended that the turning speed be low, since it is desirable to move just enough air to mix the room's atmosphere properly and introduce an adequate amount of fresh air.

While it is not always possible to precisely predict where and to what extent stratification takes place, it is present to some degree in all rooms which do not have the proper equipment to break it up. High, domed, or cathedral ceilinged rooms (Figure 2-5) are particularly prone to stratification because the warmest layers of air are able to move farther away from the coolest layers.

Figure 2-5: Cathedral ceilinged rooms are particularly prone to stratification.

It is simple to understand why air destratification can save on energy costs (Figure 2-6), especially in colder months. In most homes and apartments, the heating thermostat is located about 5′ above floor level. Unfortunately, in a room where air stratification occurs, this position may be in one of the room's cooler air layers. If this is the case, the home's heating system must run more often and at a higher temperature to maintain a comfortable temperature at the thermostat level. The heating system is forced to try to maintain a difficult balance—a balance which costs energy dollars.

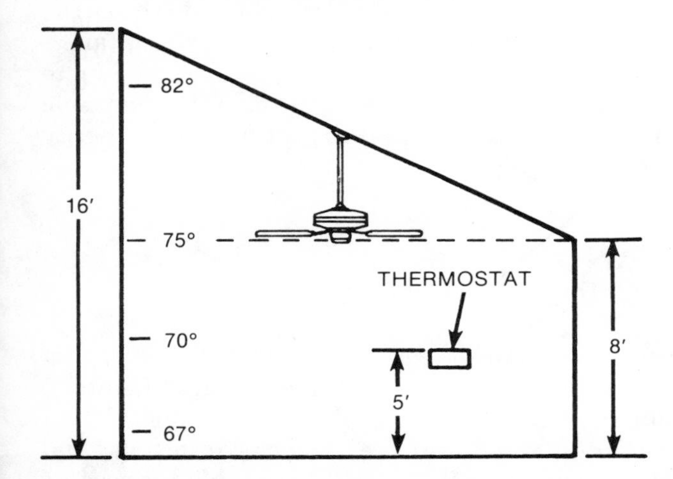

Figure 2-6: Why thermal or air stratification costs you money.

As explained previously, the action of a ceiling fan eliminates cold spots and creates a more uniform and consistent room temperature from floor to ceiling. A room's uniform temperature can be several degrees warmer than the temperature at its thermostat level prior to mixing its stratified layers. The end result of destratification is that your heating thermostat switches on less often, conserving fuel and saving you money. (Most energy "experts" agree that the average heating bill is lowered 1% to 2% for every degree you lower your thermostat in winter months.) More importantly, the level you live and work in—the first few feet above floor level—remains consistently warm and draft-free.

As with a heating system, proper air movement or circulation is essential in cooling. Cool air moves throughout your house where it picks up heat from everything it contacts, including your body. The principle of a "closed" air conditioning system is to move air mechanically to the cooling unit (air conditioner) where heat and moisture are extracted. Once cooled, the air is forced back through the house to repeat the cycle. Air conditioners can be real energy guzzlers if they are used as the **sole** source of attaining the ideal cool state.

As was mentioned earlier in this chapter, operational money savings are possible by using ceiling fans and air conditioning to complement one another. In addition, it's possible to save when installing an air conditioning unit. Here is how. The size of the air conditioning system needed for a home is based on two factors: (1) the size of the home in square feet and (2) the local climate. These two factors form the basis that air conditioning should be able to maintain an ideal room temperature of 72° on the hottest days of the year. With ceiling fans, the temperature settings can be raised and still maintain the same comfort level. If you are building a new home, you may save enough on the original cost of air conditioning units to pay for several ceiling fans.

When operating a ceiling fan in warm weather, it is necessary to operate it on medium to high speed in order to provide the desirable "windchill." Again, as in cool weather, a ceiling fan saves on energy costs without reducing your personal comfort.

CEILING FANS AND ALTERNATE ENERGY SOURCES

Besides taking steps to make more effective use of their conventional oil, gas, and electric heating systems, many consumers are turning to alternative energy sources as a means of supplying all or part of their heating needs. Freestanding wood and coal stoves, fireplaces, and solar heating systems are just some of the methods which have become popular in recent years.

When properly installed and maintained, these alternate energy heaters can certainly help reduce dependence on conventional higher priced fuels. Yet these methods do have their problems and drawbacks, many of which stem from insufficient or poor air circulation. These are the areas where ceiling fans can help.

Wood and Coal Stoves

Using a wood-burning or coal-burning stove as an effective alternative to conventional heating requires careful, well thought out planning. As with any other major home appliance, a wood or coal stove or heater can represent a sizable financial investment. In order to profit from this investment, it is crucial to select the right stove for the job and to position it for maximum heating efficiency and safety.

The stove should be placed where it is convenient to use, while still fitting comfortably into the overall design and layout of the room. Of course, the final location will be limited somewhat by the location of flue pipes and chimneys. Proper clearance between the stove and combustible materials such as walls, furniture, and wooden floors must also be maintained (Figure 2-7).

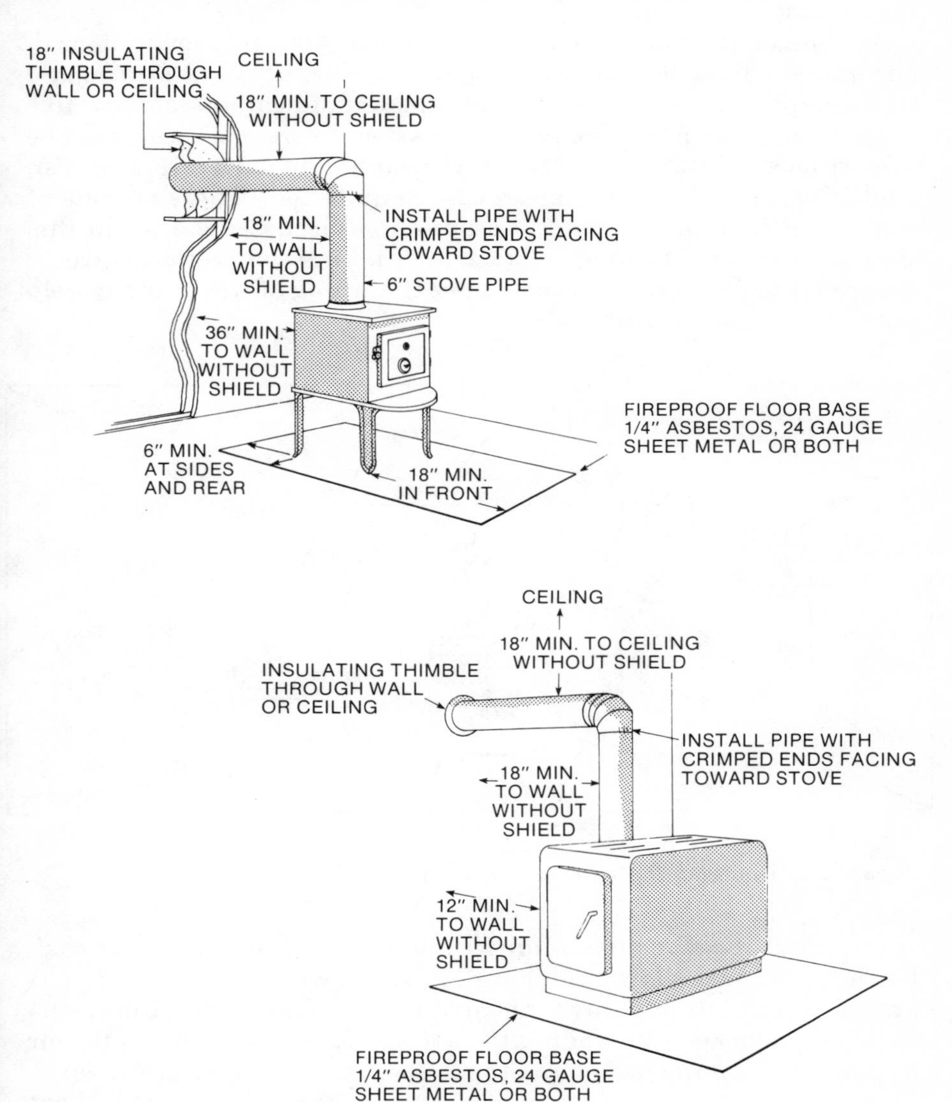

Figure 2-7: Minimum clearances from unprotected surfaces for radiating and circulating wood-burning stoves as recommended by the National Fire Protection Association (NFPA).

A stove's location in a room will also have an effect on its heating efficiency. An ideal stove location takes advantage of the optimum radiant heat transmission of a stove (Figure 2-8). Locating a stove near windows or outside walls will result in the loss of some radiant heat to the outside.

One major drawback of these small freestanding wood- or coal-burning stoves is that they are stationary "point" heat sources. So while many generate a considerable amount of heat, few stoves have any effective means of distributing this heat to areas where it may be needed most. Naturally, those areas nearest the stove are warmest, while those some distance away can be quite cool. These pockets of warm and cool air can lead to a situation discussed earlier in this chapter—air stratification. In fact, the natural convection currents generated by freestanding wood- or coal-burning stoves actually help promote air stratification.

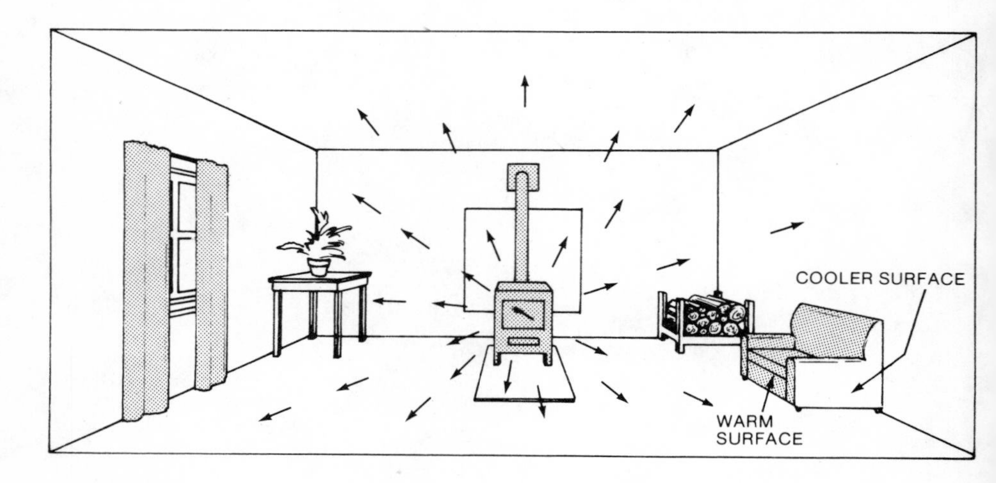

Figure 2-8: How radiant heat transmission heats a room.

The natural convection or air currents created by a wood- or coal-burning stove are shown in Figure 2-9. The stove in this illustration is known as a circulating stove or heater. Its distinguishing feature is the outer metal jacket surrounding the firebox. As the stove heats the air located between the jacket and the firebox, cold room air is drawn in through vents near the bottom of the stove, heated, and expelled out through the stove's upper vents.

As this heated air leaves the stove, it sets up a series of natural convection currents within the room. All freestanding stoves, not just cir-

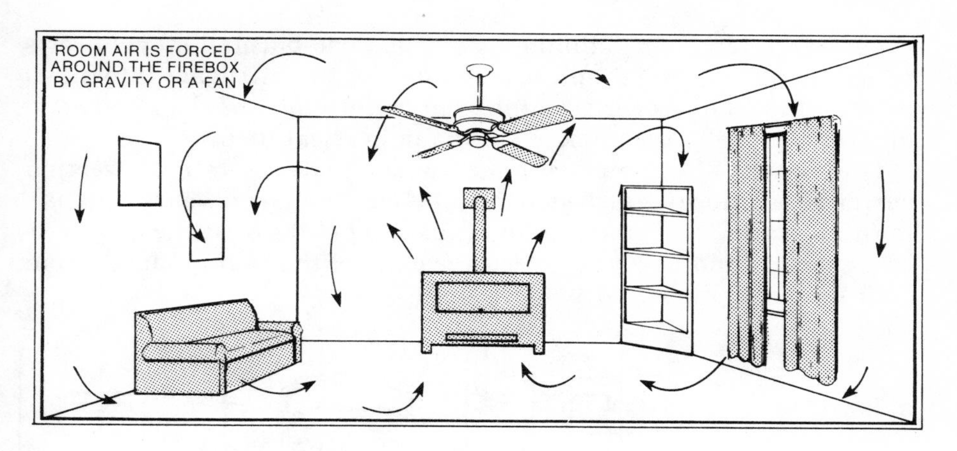

Figure 2-9: Natural convection currents created by a stove and helped by a ceiling fan.

culating styles, set up these currents. The warm air rises to the ceiling where it remains until it cools and drops back down near floor level. Once reheated, the warm air again rises to the ceiling and the cycle continues. However, in most cases—even with the circulating stoves—the natural convection action is too slow. The disadvantages of having most of the heated air near the ceiling and most of the cool air near the floor are obvious. The solution to the problem is also obvious. A ceiling fan usually installed in the center of the room can serve as a simple form of active heat recovery. When properly set, the ceiling fan can force down the heated air that naturally pools near the ceiling and help promote circulation of warm air to all corners of the room.

Woodburners and coalburners also have tremendous decorator appeal. A wide variety of old-fashioned and contemporary stylings, colors, and finishes are available from today's manufacturers. Many people enjoy taking the time and effort to restore genuine antique stoves. Whatever you may decide, matching your woodburner or coalburner with a selected fan style can create a stunning combination in your living room, kitchen, family room, or den.

Fireplaces

Fireplaces are not the most efficient heat producers. Conventional masonry fireplaces normally have an efficiency rating of about 10%. This means that of all the heat generated from the burning logs, 90% of it goes up and out the chimney. Special wood-burning stove inserts which fit into existing fireplaces can increase this efficiency into the 40 to 60% range, but a poorly maintained or designed fireplace can actually rob heat from the room, resulting in net heat **loss.**

The heat that does enter the room from a fireplace sets up convection currents like those described in the previous section on wood- and coal-burning stoves. As before, ceiling fans can help reverse these convection currents and help you get the most out of the heat produced from your fireplace (Figure 2-10).

Figure 2-10: A ceiling fan and a fireplace can create a beautiful, efficient combination.

In many cases the appearance, atmosphere, aroma, and cozy localized warmth of a fireplace outweigh its overall heating value. But this fact should never rule out the use of a ceiling fan in a fireplace setting. The two pieces accent one another beautifully, and the other cooling and air moving advantages of a ceiling fan make it a valuable addition to any room.

Ceiling Fans and Solar Heat

Solar energy systems are steadily gaining popularity as both primary and complementary heating sources. Such systems can be incorporated during the construction of new homes or during the renovation of existing structures. Like all other types of energy, solar heating has both advantages and disadvantages. Consider that the sun is a large, continuing source of free energy. Its heat is widely distributed, and using the sun as a fuel does not alter the earth's overall heat inventory or harm the environment. However, solar heat has drawbacks. For example, sunlight provides a relatively low energy source in comparison to the energy obtained from fossil fuels. Also, the sun's energy is intermittent and variable due to daily weather conditions, seasonal changes, and environmental effects.

Successful solar energy systems, whether passive or active, are specifically designed to collect, store, and distribute heat throughout the home. Properly designed and installed systems can be quite effective. In certain cases solar systems can provide between 50% and 80% of a home's heating needs. Energy savings of this magnitude certainly justify the system's initial cost. However, solar heating cannot be utilized this effectively in all cases. Before investing a substantial amount of money into a major solar heating project, it is wise to have the solar heating potential of your present home or building site appraised by a solar heating professional. Be sure you have a good idea of what your final energy savings will be before beginning construction.

As in other heating systems, ceiling fans can be employed to make more effective use of solar heat. The problems of air stratification and improper circulation affect the most specialized solar heating arrangements. As heat becomes trapped at the ceiling level, more solar energy must be utilized to obtain a proper comfort level. In order to operate a solar heating system more efficiently, the heat produced must be circulated and mixed through the cooler layers of air (Figure 2-11). Also, since passive solar heating tends to produce more heat than necessary during the summer months, a ceiling fan can help dissipate this extra heat by mixing it with cooler air and creating a windchill factor.

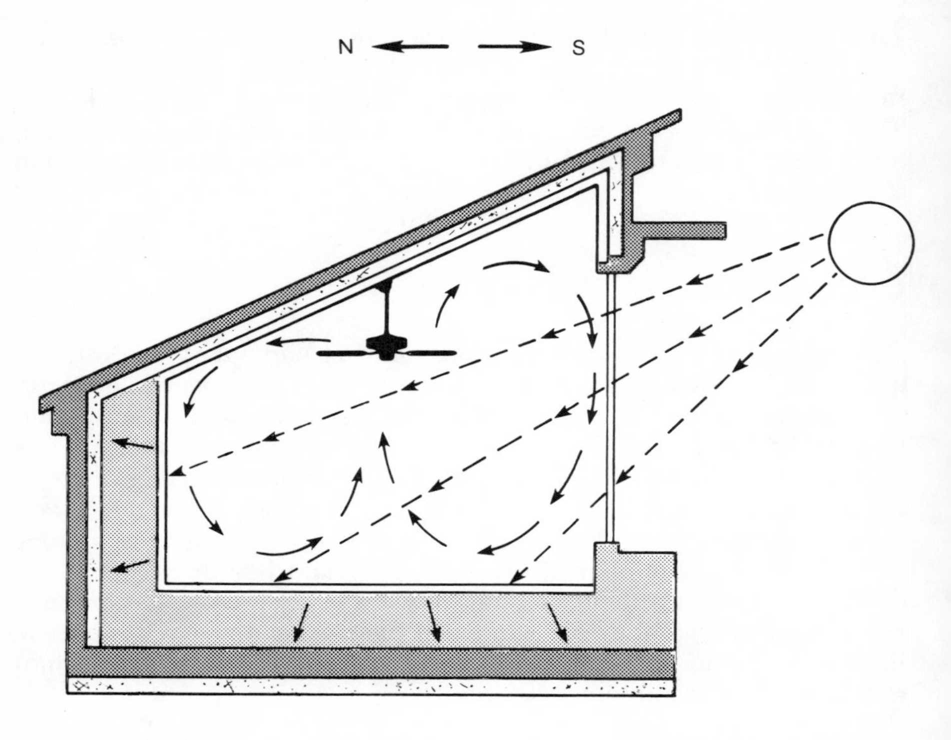

Figure 2-11: A ceiling fan will help to keep the hot air circulating in a passive solar energy system.

CEILING FANS AS ENERGY USERS

The heating and cooling energy which can be saved through the use of ceiling fans is quite impressive. But what about the energy the ceiling fan consumes while operating? The fact is a ceiling fan uses less electrical energy than the average incandescent light bulb. On the average, a modern-design ceiling fan draws as few as 9 watts of power at its lowest rate of speed and seldom more than 100 watts at its highest rate. Imagine significantly raising the comfort level of a room for less than it costs to operate a single 100-watt light bulb. The lighting accessories available for many fan styles do add a slight additional operating cost to the unit. However, since many light equipped fans are used to replace existing ceiling light fixtures, the overall increase in energy consumption is again very slight. When compared to the amount of energy saved, the amount of energy ceiling fans consume is truly insignificant.

CHAPTER 3

How to Select the Ceiling Fan for You

Today, more than 100 companies put their name on ceiling fans. A few of them actually make the fans that bear their names. However, many of them simply buy fans from factories in the Orient and affix their own names to them. It's easy. It's cheap. Some of these are tin or plastic. Some bounce about the ceiling—wobbling, whirring, and wheezing. Such ceiling fans have created a "caveat emptor" (buyer beware) attitude among many fan buyers.

To protect yourself from poorly designed and constructed fans, you must know what to look for in order to select a quality fan. Actually, a ceiling fan is a very simple appliance having three major parts—the motor, the blades, and the controls. Figure 3-1 shows the other fan components with which you should be familiar. But, before taking a look at these components, keep in mind that the type of fan you purchase involves personal taste and energy efficiency. Is the fan's aesthetic appeal uppermost, or is its energy efficiency? Can you have your cake and eat it too—an energy-efficient fan with decorative appeal? First, determine how many fans you want throughout the house and in which rooms (see Chapter 4). How big are the rooms (length, width, and height)? Are there any problems with electrical availability? What fans would best complement your decor? Then, find a **reputable** ceiling fan dealer. For now, however, let's consider the components that the dealer will be discussing with you.

MOTOR

A motor is defined as a machine that converts electrical energy into mechanical energy, usually in the form of rotational motion. Thou-

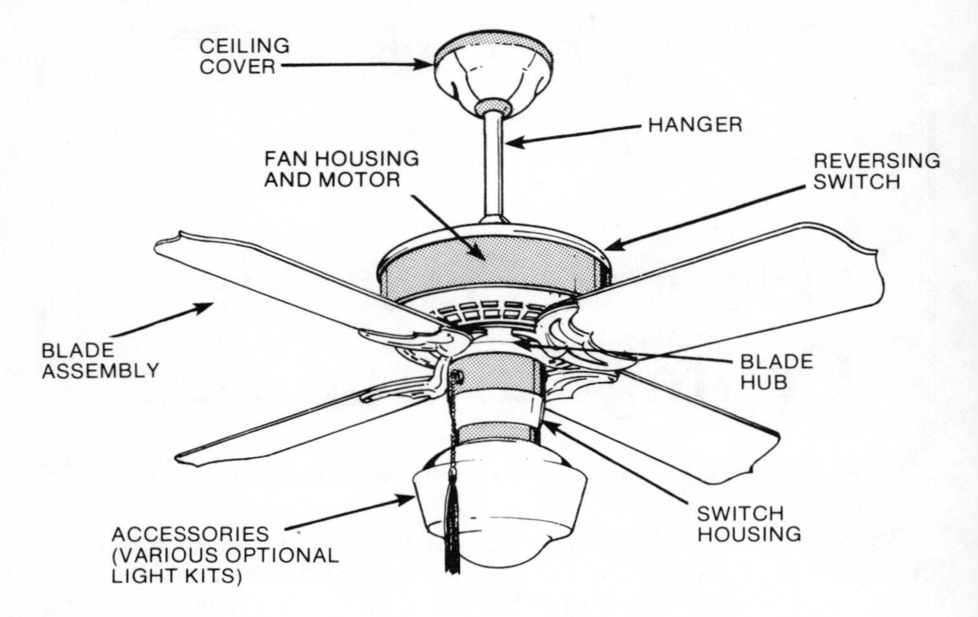

Figure 3-1: Major parts and components of a typical ceiling fan.

sands of books have been written on the theory of motor operation, but only the true "motor enthusiast" needs to understand the electromagnetic principles that these books contain when buying a ceiling fan.

Simply stated, a motor consists of two basic parts—a rotor and a stator (Figure 3-2). The name rotor is related to its function—rotation. The rotor is attached via a shaft to the fan blades. The stationary half of a motor, or stator, converts electrical current into a magnetic field, causing the rotor to turn. The components of a well-made ceiling fan motor can be seen in Figure 3-3.

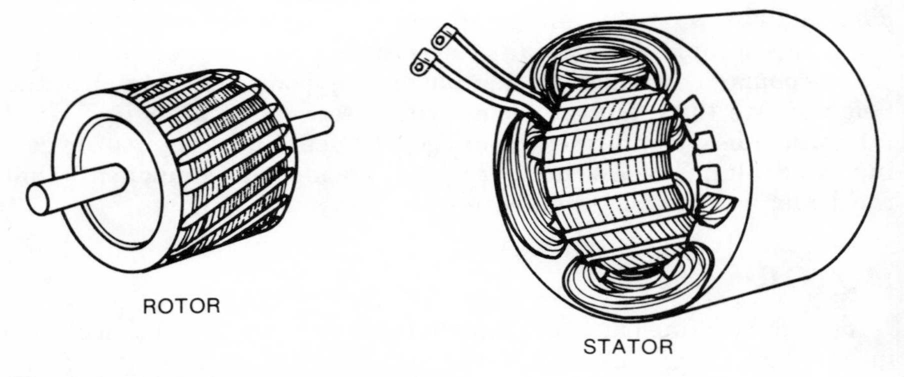

Figure 3-2: Principal motor parts.

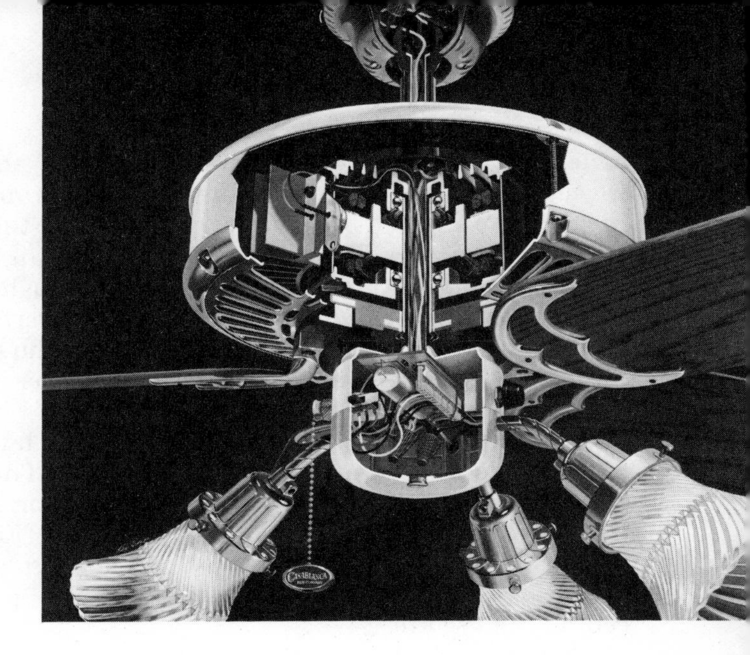

Figure 3-3: A well-constructed ceiling fan motor and its components.

In general the rotor is surrounded by the stator; however, the opposite configuration does exist. Motors such as this are simply referred to as "inside-out" motors. Many small blade fans commonly use this arrangement.

The stator is composed of poles. A pole is an electromagnet; its function is to transform electricity into magnetic energy. The speed of a motor is determined by the poles causing the rotor to spin and is measured in RPM (revolutions per minute).

Synchronous speed is the maximum RPM a motor is capable of obtaining under ideal conditions. Synchronous speed may be calculated using this simple formula:

$$\text{Synchronous Speed (RPM)} = \frac{7{,}200}{\text{number of poles}}$$

(**Note:** 7,200 is found by multiplying U.S. household current, 60 hertz, by 60 seconds in one minute by 2.) Remember, this is a theoretical figure. Actual motor RPM is affected by friction, weight of fan blades, and other external load factors.

When choosing the correct motor for a specific application, motor efficiency must be considered. This is a simple ratio of work out to work into the motor.

$$\text{Efficiency} = \frac{\text{Work Out}}{\text{Work In}} = \frac{\text{Mechanical Energy from Motor}}{\text{Electrical Energy to Motor}}$$

Electric motors exist in two basic forms—universal and induction motors. The means of rotor excitement (starting rotation) is the major difference. When physical contact between the rotor and stator, through "brushes" or "commutator bars," transfers electricity, the motor is a universal type. Following transfer, the conversion to magnetic energy occurs. These motors obtain very high speeds, up to 15,000 RPM, and require periodic replacement of brushes. One drawback of this motor is the creation of radio frequency interference (RFI) which is commonly observed as some form of TV or radio static. Typical installation of the universal motor includes power tools, blenders, and vacuum cleaners.

Ceiling fans use an induction motor of which there are two types—shaded-pole and permanent split capacitor. The shaded-pole motor incorporates at least two poles within the stator. A heavy copper loop, the shading ring, surrounds one end of the pole (Figure 3-4). These coils aid in starting the motor by delaying the magnetic flow. Some of the advantages and disadvantages of the shaded-pole type of motor for ceiling fan use are:

1. Efficiency is low, only 20 to 40%.
2. Two shaded poles are necessary to allow for reversibility. Some large blade fans do not have a reverse feature.
3. This motor is quiet and dependable, and it has a long life. It is often used in direct-drive air moving situations.
4. Construction is simple, cutting cost in large production runs.

A permanent split capacitor (PSC) motor has one pole connected directly to the power source while the other pole is connected through a capacitor. A capacitor is a specialized electrical device working like the shaded ring, its function being for starting purposes only (Figure 3-5).

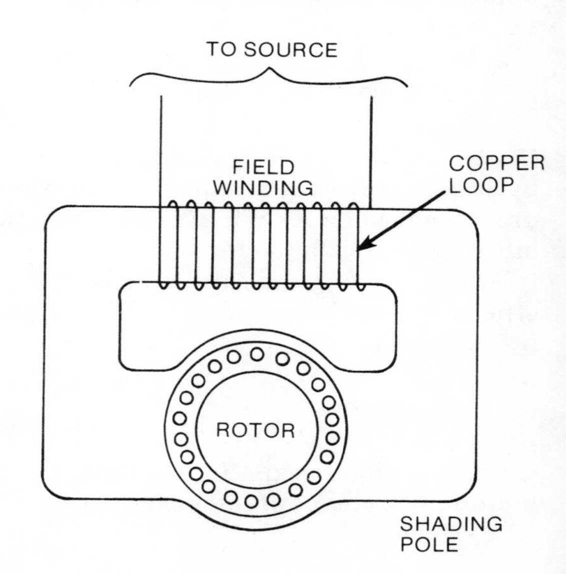

Figure 3-4: Diagram of a shaded-pole induction motor.

The advantages and disadvantages of the PSC motor in ceiling fans are:

1. Efficiency is relatively high, around 50 to 70%.
2. Frequent or rapid reversing is easily accomplished.
3. Torque is low, limiting application to light starting loads.
4. Assembly of the motor is more complex; therefore, production costs increase.

For these reasons, modern-design ceiling fans use PSC motors.

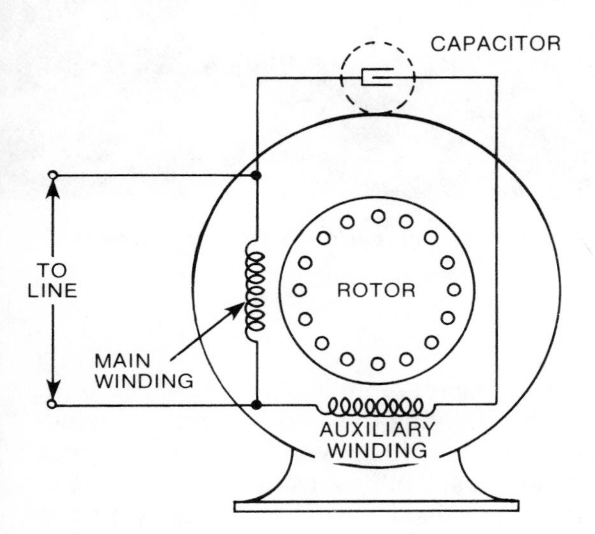

Figure 3-5: Diagram of a permanent split capacitor induction motor.

When selecting a ceiling fan, look for such motor and motor housing features as a "maintenance free" unit that has precision lifetime bearings that never need oiling, heavy-duty construction but light in weight for easy handling and installation, quiet operation of the motor, rugged metal motor housing, and an attractive appearance (Figure 3-6). In fact, most reliable fan manufacturers have several types of housing and housing finishes available. They range from bright chrome, copper, and brass to antique finishes of copper, brass, and pewter. There are also painted finishes of antique white, traditional brown, and charcoal black.

One other word about fan motors and their warranties—we've learned from the auto industry that biggest is not best; likewise, in fan warranties, "longest is not always most lasting!" There are many warranty types from lifetime to 15 years to 5 years. The real question about a warranty is not the length of the warranty itself, but the company behind it. Are they known for dependability and commitment to the fan industry? Usually, a five year warranty on working parts is adequate protection.

Figure 3-6: A motor housing can be a very important part of a ceiling fan's beauty.

FAN BLADES

Fan blades are both a "thing of beauty" and a functional fan part. They perform the important job of moving the air, creating the "wind-chill," and reclaiming the heat at ceiling level during the winter. Blades are available in several sizes, ranging from about 16″ to 21″ (Figure 3-7). Among the things to consider when selecting your fan blades are the material used for their construction, shaping, flatness, color, and decorative trim.

Blade Material. Most fans on the market today are made of wood (solid, plywood, and composites), plastic, and metal.

Because of their aesthetic appeal and beauty, solid wood fan blades are the most popular. They are usually from 3/16″ to 1/4″ thick. (Underwriter's Laboratories [UL] now require all blade thicknesses at 3/16″ minimum.) Basswood and poplar are the two common species used. Oak, walnut, teak, and cherry are available at higher cost.

Plywood blades are usually constructed of an interior grade plywood and are available in the same basic thicknesses as solid wood. The veneer surfaces are generally made of rich hardwoods. The nature of plywood construction has a tendency to reduce warpage in a typical residential installation.

The third category of "wood" blades consists of wood composites such as hardboard and particleboard. These blades are usually less expensive than solid wood and plywood, but thanks to a wood grain vinyl overlay glued to both sides, they have the same basic appearance.

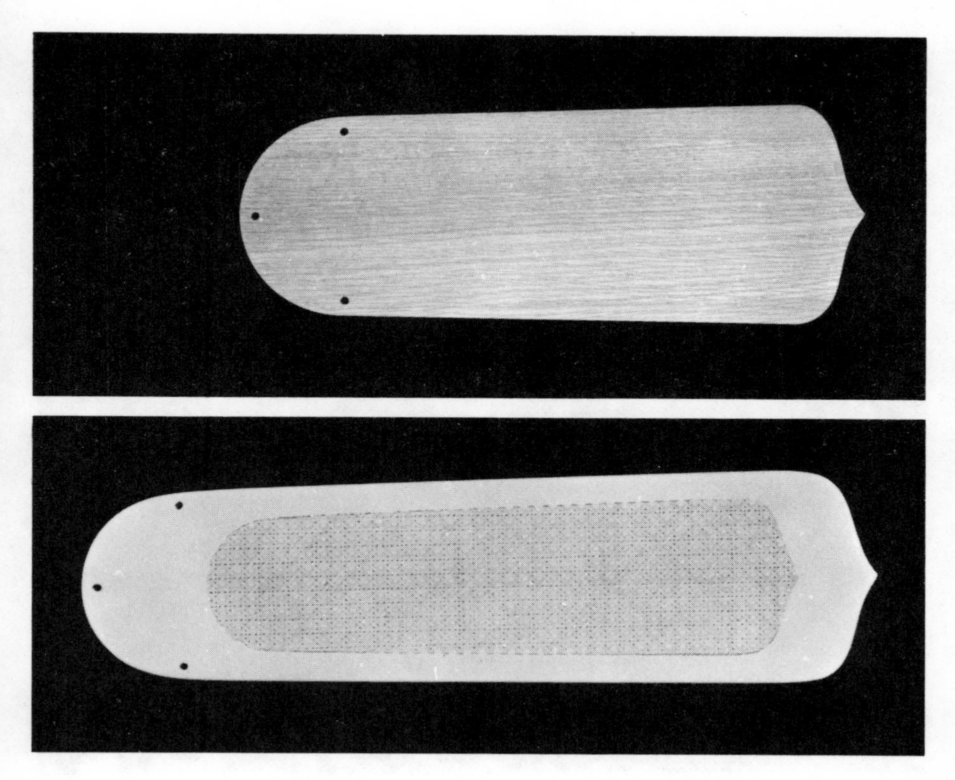

Figure 3-7: A "short" fan blade (top) and "long" fan blade (bottom).

Plastic blades are available either in a transparent acrylic form or in simulated wood finish. For the latter blades, impact-resistant polystyrene is commonly used to mold blades because it is easily textured and painted. Plastic blades are slightly cheaper than wood but sometimes warp from their own weight. If thin plastic blades are used, they have a tendency to "flap" when they are in motion.

Metal blades, usually aluminum, are found on "economy" ceiling fans and on industrial fans that require good air-moving characteristics under rugged environmental conditions.

Blade Aesthetics. Ceiling fan blades are decorated in several ways, the most common finish being a stained and lacquered finish (Figure 3-8A). This treatment allows for an unlimited number of colors to be offered. Oak blades usually receive a second color coat which is hand rubbed, increasing the visibility of grain along with cost.

The most popular option offered in fan blades is the cane insert (Figure 3-8B). During final processing cane is imbedded into the blade, adding an "antique" touch to the fan. This finish is costlier due to extra materials and handling.

Gold and silver pinstriping is another common finish (Figure 3-8C). Scrollwork is applied to the blade by stamping with a hot press. These transfers are applied easily with little added cost to the consumer.

Antique white (Figure 3-8D) and painted are other popular finishes.

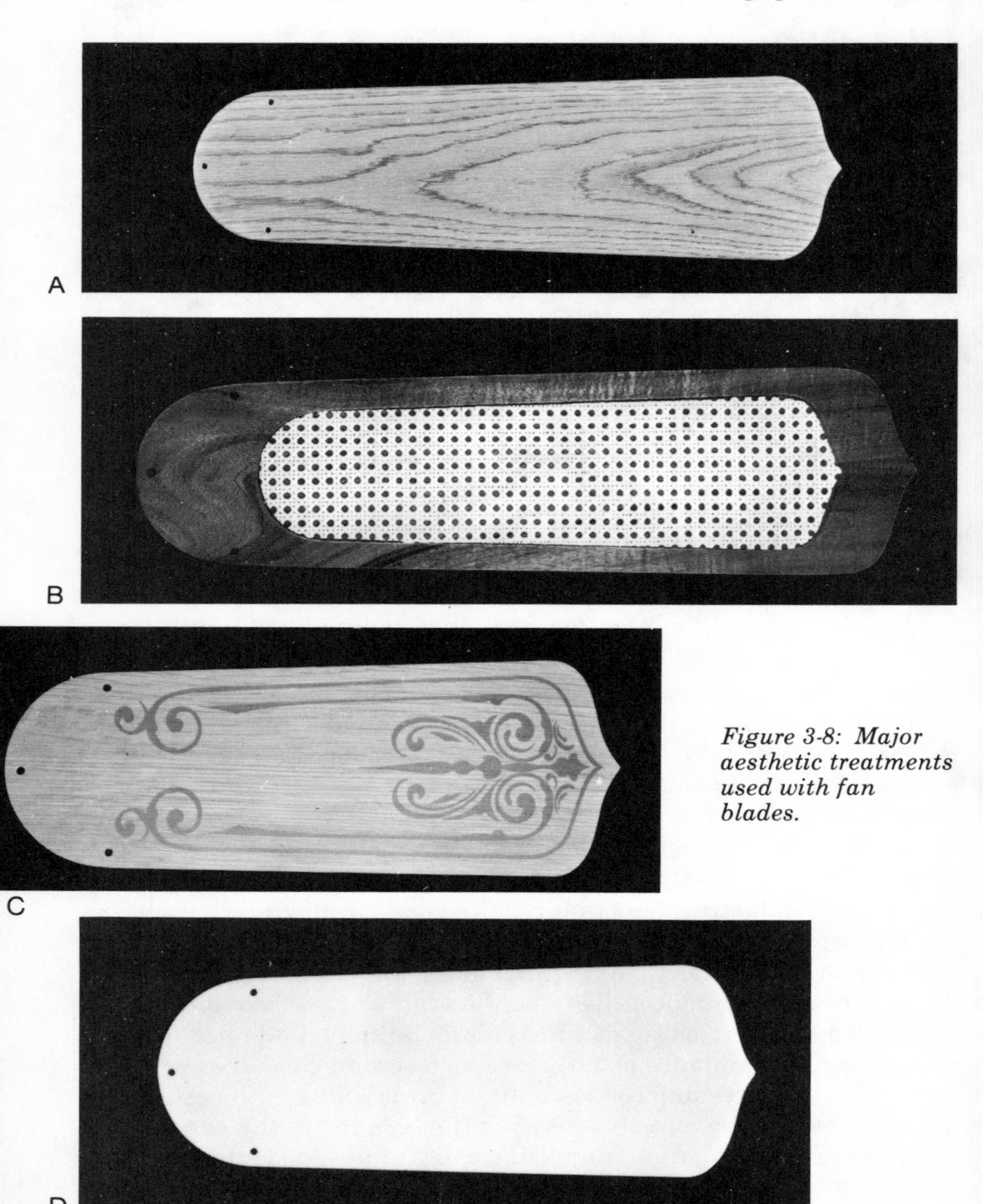

Figure 3-8: Major aesthetic treatments used with fan blades.

Blade Warpage and Balancing. For a fan to perform efficiently and effectively, it is very important that the blade be flat throughout the life of the unit. Because of this, blade warpage is a major concern of fan manufacturers. Finding it impractical, in terms of time and money, to test blades under residential conditions, laboratory environments have been created to conduct accelerated warpage tests. Most reliable fan manufacturers have accelerated programs to investigate all possible means of keeping warpage to a minimum.

Most quality fans have "balanced" blades; that is, the blades are carefully balanced electronically at the factory and are sold as balanced sets of four or five blades—depending on the design of the fan (Figure 3-9). For this reason, never interchange blades between fans.

Figure 3-9: Four-blade fan (above) and five-blade fan (below).

When selecting or installing fan blades, check the warpage by sighting down the edge of the blade as if aiming a rifle (Figure 3-10). If warping appears too great, refuse the blades or take the blade set back to your dealer.

In recent years, the classic decorative beauty of the five-blade fan has come into vogue. Some manufacturers have kits (Figure 3-11) available for those who wish to convert their present four-blade ceiling fan to a five-blade type.

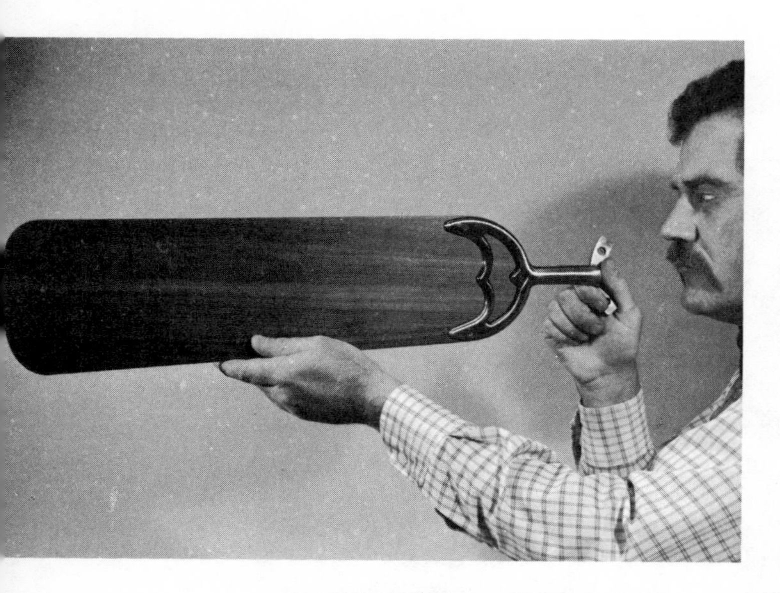

Figure 3-10: Checking blade warpage.

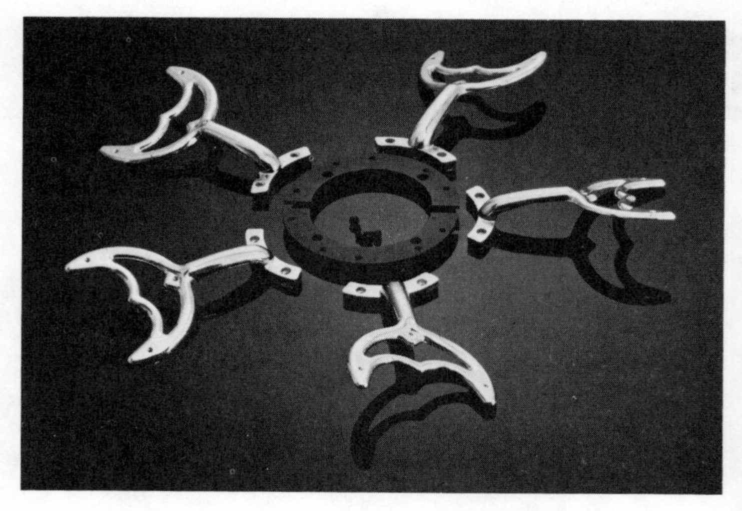

Figure 3-11: Typical five-blade kit.

CONTROLS

Ceiling fan controls vary in complexity from a simple ON/OFF switch to a complex wireless "remote" control that varies lighting level and regulates fan speed. By definition, a control is a mechanism which regulates machine operation.

In order for your ceiling fan to operate, a complete path is needed between two sides of a 120-volt electrical supply. Circuits are identified as being either a parallel or series type (Figure 3-12). In order for you to be able to control your fan, switches are placed into these circuits.

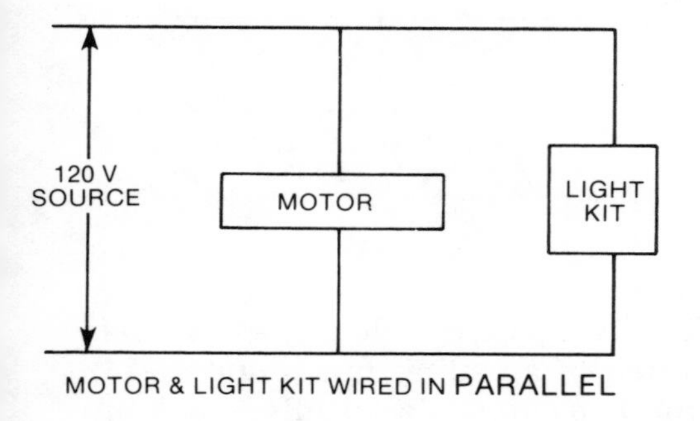

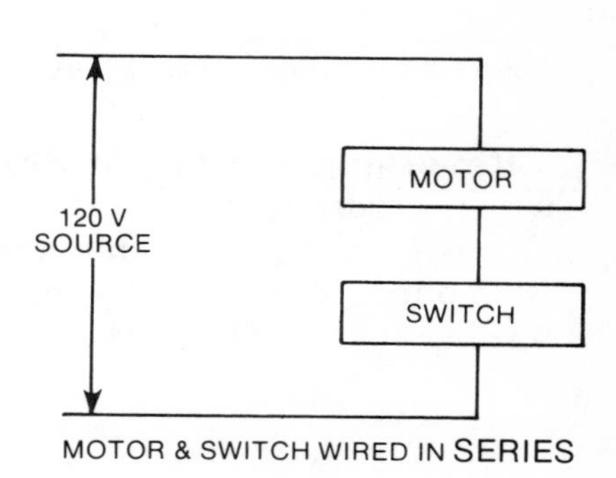

Figure 3-12: Two hookups used in fan wiring.

Switches

The basic function of a switch is to interrupt or complete an electric circuit. There are two general types of switches used in fan construction: single-pole, single-throw (SPST) and single-pole, double-throw (SPDT). Single-throw or position switches have one conducting position; the switch is either ON or OFF (Figure 3-13A). Double-throw switches have two conducting positions (Figure 3-13B). A switch which controls only one conductor is known as a single-pole, while one controlling two conductors is a double-pole type (Figure 3-13C).

ON/OFF Switch. In ceiling fan applications, the single-pole, single-throw (SPST) type switch is the ON/OFF switch. A single conductor is either broken or connected by the action of the switch. Maximum amperage and voltage for safe operation are regulated by Underwriters' Laboratories (UL). Make sure all switches in your fan are UL approved.

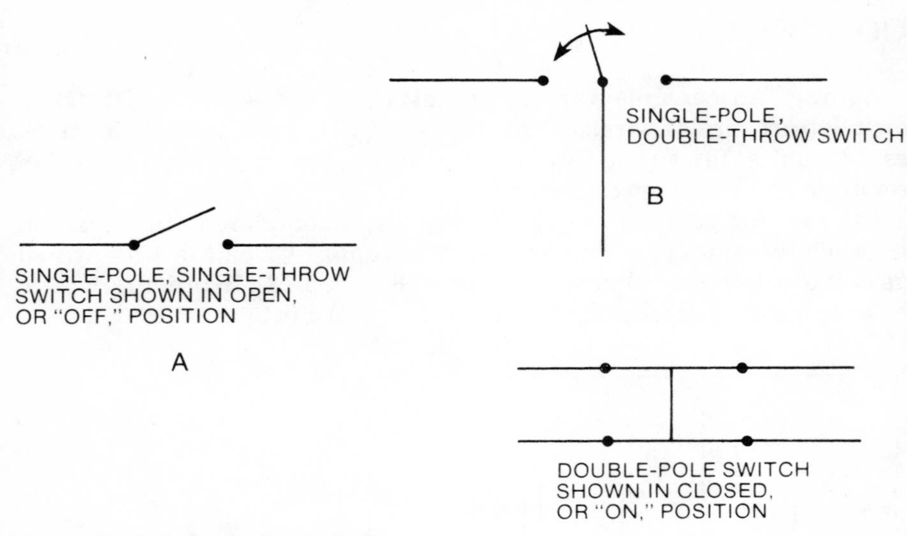

Figure 3-13: Principal switch types.

Reversing Switch. An SPDT (single-pole, double-throw) switch is used in order to reverse the rotation of a ceiling fan (Figure 3-14). Throwing the switch changes the capacitor (electrically speaking) from one motor coil to the other, reversing the direction the rotor is turning.

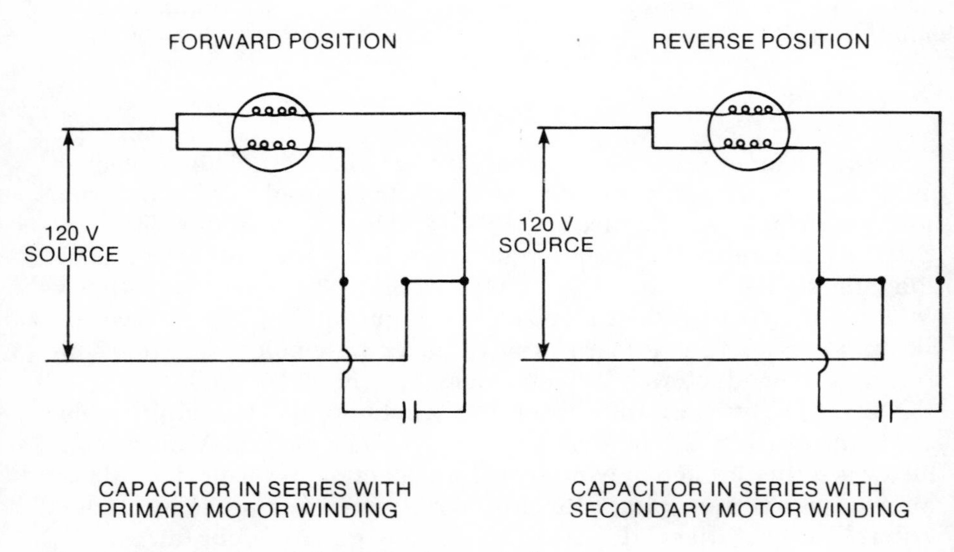

Figure 3-14: Action of the reversing switch.

Speed Controls

Fan blade speed is regulated by controlling the voltage to the motor. As the voltage is reduced, the fan's speed is slowed. Lowered voltage reduces the RPM of a fan. A speed control's primary function is to adjust RPM. While there are several speed controls on the market, the three most common are solid-state, inductive, and choke types.

Ceiling fan noise can be a serious problem in some locations. It was this that prompted fan manufacturers to use electronic speed controls.

All permanent-split capacitor induction motors are designed to operate with a smooth sine wave input from an electrical power line (Figure 3-15A). Most commercially available inductive type motor controls vary the power by chopping the sine wave 120 times a second (Figures 3-15B and C).

While this technique is simple and efficient, motors are not tolerant of it. Sharp torsional pulsations are generated which must be dampened. Otherwise, significant noise will be generated. While various dampening devices have been tried (including the so-called silent flex hub), none have been completely successful because:

- They are not quiet enough for bedroom use.
- They are inconsistent from one fan to another.
- They typically worsen as the fan ages.

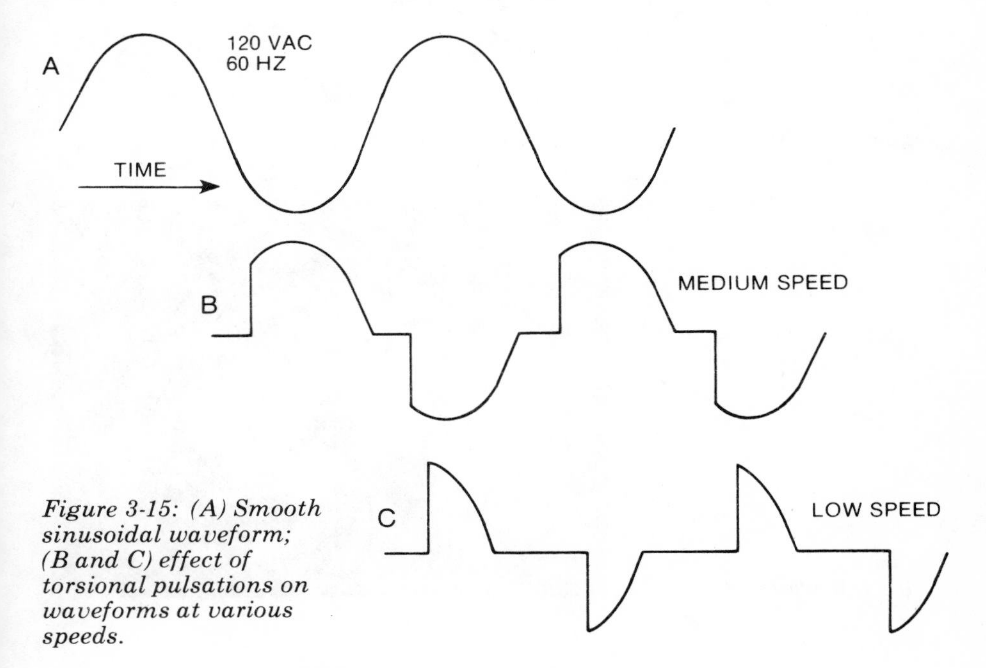

Figure 3-15: (A) Smooth sinusoidal waveform; (B and C) effect of torsional pulsations on waveforms at various speeds.

Quality solid-state controls—usually located on the fan housings themselves—employ a positive method of eliminating torsional pulsations. They vary the power to the motor by varying the **amplitude** of the sine wave, maintaining the smooth wave shape the motor was designed for (Figure 3-16). Some quality fans achieve this effect at three speeds via capacitance control or transformers, while others accomplish amplitude control at a continuously variable speed via a power transistor. These are the two most successful means.

Where a wall speed control is desired, the solid-state inductive control that regulates the voltage input via the use of electronic components is the most common (Figure 3-17). The heart of this control is a device known as a triac or bi-directional silicon-controlled rectifier. As previously mentioned, this control regulates voltage by removing a por-

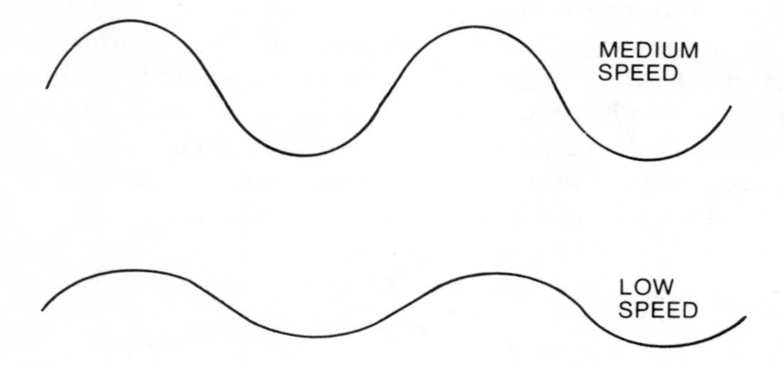

Figure 3-16: Waveforms under amplitude control.

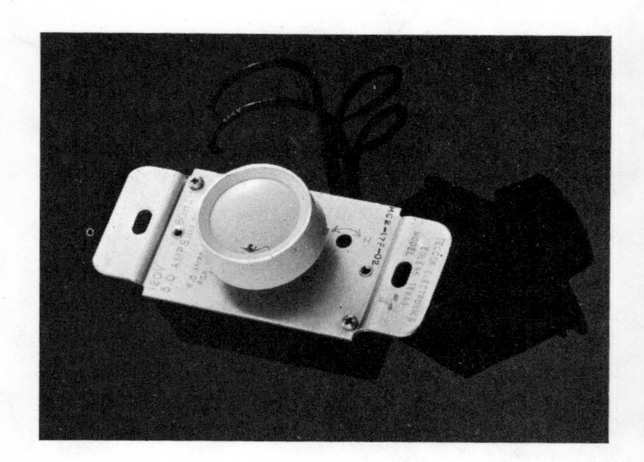

Figure 3-17: Typical solid-state wall control.

tion of the sinusoidal (sine) waveform. Motor hum associated with this type of control is due to rapid voltage change.

The choke type control employs many feet of copper wire wrapped around a metal core. By "tapping" into this wire (connecting into the coil at different locations), differing coils can be derived from one coil; the five-speed controls have a tapped coil design. As the rotary switch is rotated from "off" (no electrical circuit) through "high" (no coil in electrical circuit) to "low" (maximum coil in circuit), increasing resistance is added to the circuit, "choking" the motor. The choke control reduces the voltage to the motor without altering the sinusoidal waveform, thus allowing the motor to operate quietly (without hum). But, choke controls **do** tend to heat up during normal operations due to their design. They also extend several inches from the wall, considered unattractive by many.

All speed controls are wired in a "series" electrical circuit with the ceiling fan. Since electrical current (amps) is constant in the speed control and ceiling fan motor, it is important the UL current rating of the controller is **equal to or greater than** the current rating of the ceiling fan. For instance, most wall controls are designed to simultaneously control from 4 to 8 amps of ceiling fan electrical current. Wiring diagrams appear on the instruction sheet. It's important to note current ratings of the fans are **additive** when fans are wired as instructed. For example, if three fans, each rated at 1.5 amps, are to be controlled simultaneously by one 4-amp control, it is within the proper current range (1.5 + 1.5 + 1.5 amps = 4.5 amps). If a fourth fan is then wired in with the initial three, the installation is improper and could lead to control damage and possibly a dangerous situation. When lighting is also used, this current must also be added. Divide total wattage by 120 to get amps (240 watts ÷ 120 VAC = 2 amps).

Specialty Controls

There are several specialty controls on the market that are available for use with ceiling fans. These are usually available as options and include:

Light Dimmer Switches. The infinite number of wall speed controls referred to shouldn't be confused with a light dimmer switch sold in most hardware and electrical stores. Most light switches of this type are clearly labeled "for incandescent use only" and are not suitable for fan motor control. Motor overheating and damage may occur if such a switch is improperly used.

Temperature Modulated Fan Speed Control. This control automatically changes fan speeds in conjunction with temperature changes. Remember, differing activities, humidity, and personal comfort dictate a wide variance of fan cooling at a given temperature.

Remote Control. This unit is a wireless control similar to those found on many home televisions. It features fan speed and light intensity control from any location in the room.

Remote Wall Control. This unit is a wired control system that offers complete control over fan speed and reversal plus light dimming. Other security and energy saving features are included. These units work over existing household wiring and take the place of the standard light switches.

CHAPTER 4

Locations for Your Ceiling Fan

Ceiling fans are designed for use in places other than "Nick's Near-East Cafe" and old-fashioned ice cream parlors (Figure 4-1). The decorative value of ceiling fans has been recognized and they are now available in a wide variety of styles, materials, and colors. Elegantly designed ceiling fans with antique brass trim are suitable for formal living and dining rooms (Figure 4-2). Country styled fans featuring attractive light shades add a decorative touch in game rooms or country kitchens (Figure 4-3). A white paddled fan would be perfect for a porch or patio area done in white wicker (Figure 4-4). Ceiling fans reflect your personal taste. Decorating with them is an energy-saving way to brighten every room in the house.

Figure 4-1: Ceiling fans have long been a favorite in cafes and ice cream parlors.

Figure 4-2: Ceiling fans are at home in formal living and dining rooms.

Figure 4-3: The country kitchen is an ideal location for a ceiling fan.

Figure 4-4: The five-blade Panama fan blends well with the white wicker furniture.

Remember, in most instances the ceiling fan will be the first item noticed in a room. Its physical location, usually centered, as well as the movement of the blades will catch the eye. In your den or recreation area a brass fan will highlight paneling and masonry. Furniture trim may also affect your decision. Brass knobs and hinges will be complimented by a brass fan; silver tone items may not.

Be careful in noting ceiling height. A fan with a lighter finish will show those who visit you the thoughtfulness with which you have decorated your home. Most quality ceiling fans can be tailored to your taste. Don't compromise with just the "efficient" or just the "beautiful." Select a fan that is beautifully efficient. They are available. Also, practice a little "caveat emptor" and you'll find the one fan for you.

As you can see, selecting a ceiling fan takes serious consideration. In addition to room decor, the size and number of ceiling fans and their locations are key factors. Remember, don't **skimp** on numbers, or your ceiling fan investment may pay inadequate dividends in comfort and energy savings; in other words, the optimum investment pays optimum dividends.

FAN SIZE

Most people select a fan size and style that visually blends well with the room. With some ceiling fans, it's possible to mix and match blade and fan housings to get a variety of sizes. However, to obtain the best results from a ceiling fan, it's important to keep a few facts in mind.

For instance, a house can be divided into four major classifications or living areas: bedrooms, kitchens, living/family rooms, and other areas (utility rooms, porches, basements, garages). Each of these areas has its own distinct occupancy pattern and, thus, different cooling requirements are needed from the fans. Table 4-1 is a compilation of available data for recommended sizing and location of ceiling fans in the basic living areas. This table should be used to make an **approximate** recommendation for fan installation for applications where cooling is the primary function of the fan. Due to assumptions on differing human comfort levels (Figure 4-5), varying fan locations, and differing environmental factors (such as humidity and wall radiation temperatures), these recommendations cannot be guaranteed 100% accurate for all installations. Generally, a fan with a 38″ span is usually capable of handling areas up to 12′ by 15′. However, a fan with a larger blade sweep will also work well in this size room at a much lower

Table 4-1: Recommended Fan Size and Location

Room	Typical Activities	Recommended Location	Alternate Location	Minimum Fan Size	Ambient Air Temperature*
Bedroom	Sleeping	Over foot of bed	Off to either side of bed, but not directly over head of bed.	36″—up to 150 sq. ft. 48″—up to 300 sq. ft. 52″—up to 600 sq. ft.	86°F
Living Family Dining	Sitting, walking, light housework	Center of room	In corner, minimum 24″ blade tip clearance from wall	Same as above	78°F
Kitchen	Cooking, washing dishes	Center of room	Away from stove	Same as above	76°F
Garage Utility	Light work	Center of room	In corner, minimum 24″ blade tip clearance from wall	Same as above	See Figure 4-5

*Maximum temperature at which occupants maintain "72°F comfort level" with fan in operation.

speed and with less air noise. Because of the variable speed feature available in most well-designed fans, a unit with a large blade span can be adjusted to perform perfectly in a smaller space.

As a general rule, an average size living room, patio, or dining room would be best suited with a fan that has a blade sweep of 48″ or over. For an average size bedroom, a fan with a 48″ blade sweep should be correct. This size fan will also work well in the average kitchen, sunroom, den, or similarly sized room. If you have an area in your home that is 9′ by 12′ with an 8′ ceiling or higher, a 36″ to 48″ tip to tip span blade is adequate; this might be a child's bedroom or a den. For a larger area such as a dining room leading into a living room 12′ by 18′ with an 8′ or higher ceiling, a larger fan, preferably a 48″ or 52″ span is best (Figure 4-6). A larger fan will draw less electricity to do its job. A smaller fan would have to work harder and be set on a higher blade speed. Never undersize a fan. If in doubt, it is better to go to the larger blade size.

Keep in mind that large areas should have two or more 52″ fans. For example, the average three-bedroom house with approximately 2,000 square feet of living space could need three fans strategically located (Figure 4-7) to deliver optimum energy efficiency and personal comfort.

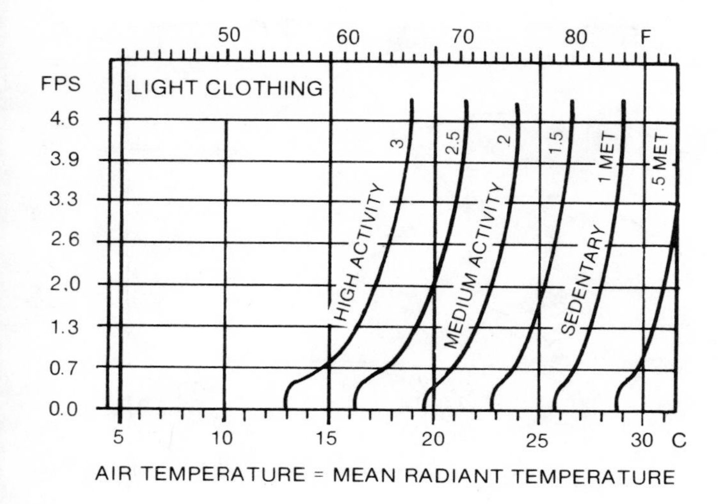

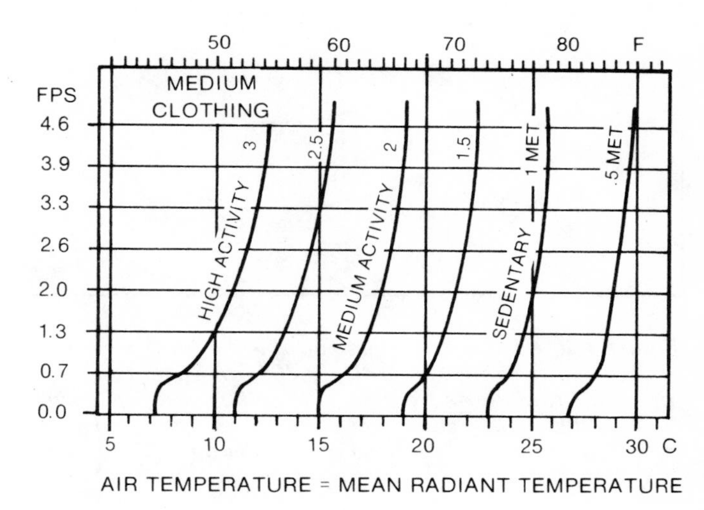

MET = .8 SLEEP
1.0 SITTING
2.25 LIGHT HOUSEWORK
3.25 MODERATE TO HEAVY WORK

Figure 4-5: The comfort lines corresponding to three different activity levels. These are curves through different combinations of relative air velocity and ambient temperature which provide optimal thermal comfort. The work performed (expressed in terms of "MET number") is approximate for the activity cited. **Source: ASHRAE Handbook.**

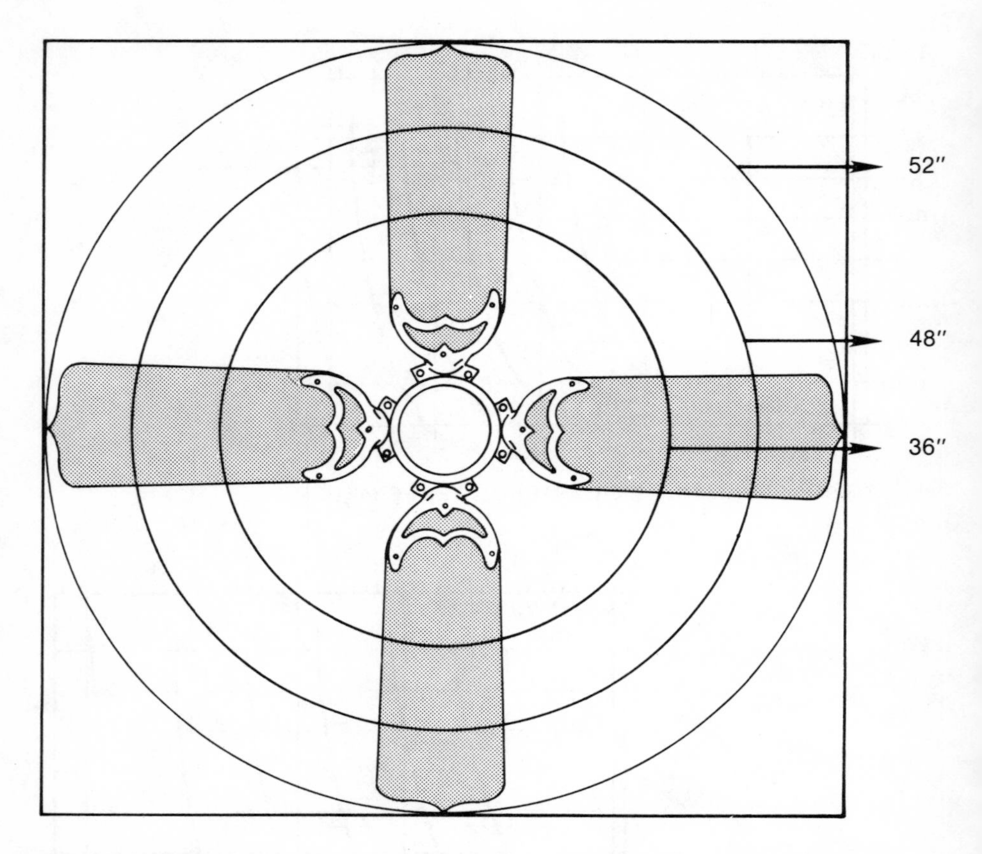

Figure 4-6: A 52" fan is most suitable for large rooms or patios where more airflow is desirable. Generally, a 36" fan displaces 2,500 to 4,000 cubic feet of air. A 48" fan moves from 4,000 to 8,000 cubic feet of air. A 52" fan circulates from 4,000 to 9,000 cubic feet of air. A 48" fan is good for any room up to 15' by 18'. A 38" fan is best used in rooms up to 12' by 15' in size.

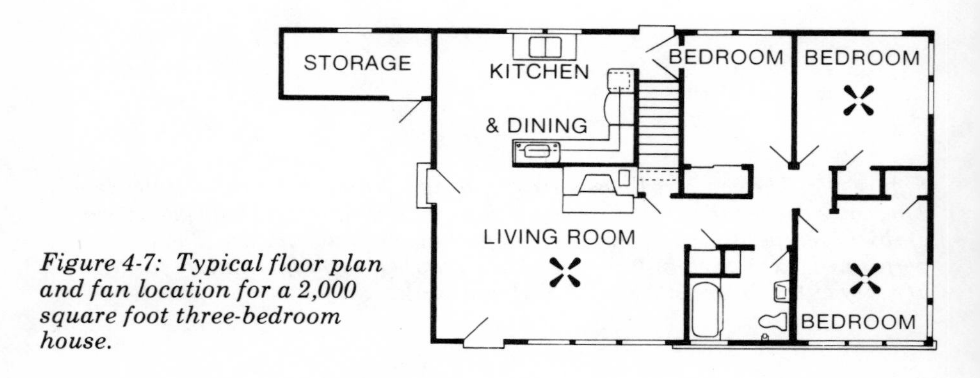

Figure 4-7: Typical floor plan and fan location for a 2,000 square foot three-bedroom house.

AIR CIRCULATION AND VELOCITY

Ceiling fans, as they are known today, are designed primarily to circulate air in a "closed" environment. The typical airflow patterns shown in Figure 4-8 for flat and sloped ceilings indicate how the air movement travels around a room when the blades are set in their down-

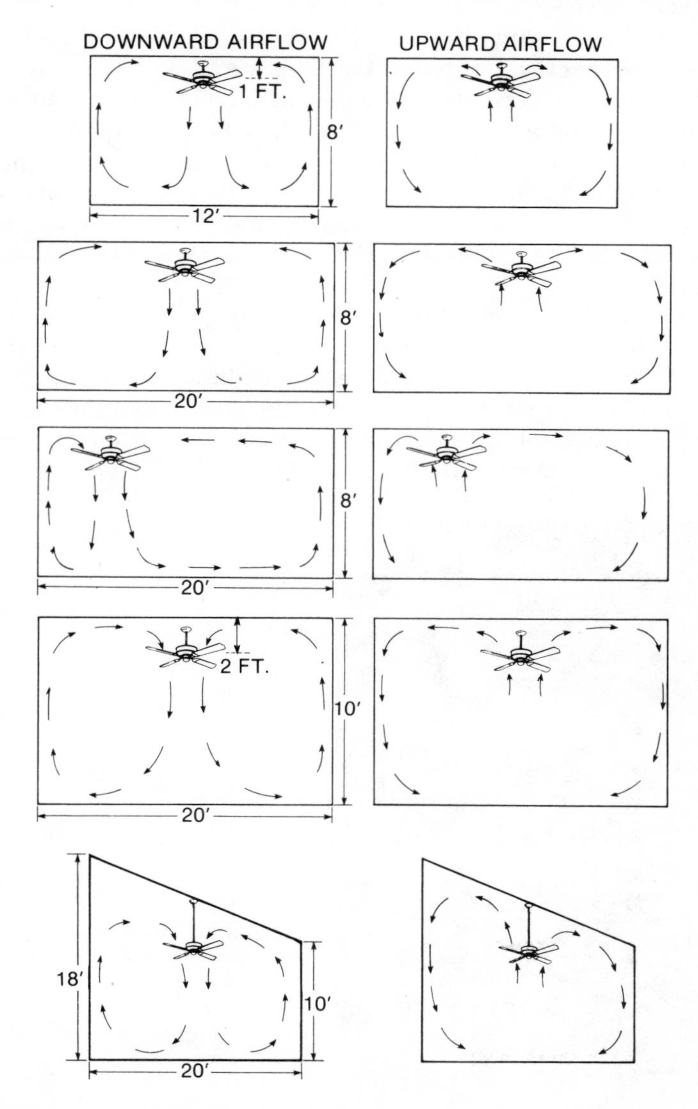

Figure 4-8: Typical airflow patterns.

ward and upward positions. The downward airflow over your skin has a cooling effect that is most desirable in warm weather. In cooler weather, an upward airflow recovers the wasted heat trapped at the ceiling. This homogenizing of the room's air eliminates cold spots and drafts.

When considering the size and location, it is important to remember that a ceiling fan affects subjects that fall into two distinct categories:

- subjects directly under the ceiling fan
- subjects in the same room as the ceiling fan.

Subjects Directly Under a Ceiling Fan. This situation occurs in offices where workers sit at their desks, in restaurants where patrons sit at tables, at home in bed, or in the den where occupants sit in their favorite reading chairs (Figure 4-9). These applications are the easiest to understand and study, since it requires little in the way of test equipment sophistication. The earlier cited studies conclude an adult situated under a fan can tolerate a maximum air velocity of about 6 FPS comfortably.

Subjects in the Same Room as a Ceiling Fan. Many considerations must be taken into account when sizing ceiling fans for whole room cooling applications. Since no work has been done to date on complete airflow in an enclosed room, the recommendations made in this chapter are a combination of technical data and common sense. As you'll note in Figure 4-10, the size and height of a room also have a

Figure 4-9: In the den, the fan can be right over the piano.

bearing on airflow pattern. As a general rule, the larger the room area and the higher the ceiling, the greater the volume of air that must be moved. This can be accomplished by increasing the speed of the fan's blades or by increasing the blade length.

In addition to the time of year, the location of your ceiling fan has a bearing on the airflow pattern. When a ceiling fan is installed over a breakfast or dining table, for instance, an upward airflow pattern is suggested. A downward airflow (Figure 4-11A) would tend to quickly cool the meal. With an upward airflow pattern (Figure 4-11B), the air is blown down the walls and returns to the fan in an upward flow, across the people sitting around the table. Should you wish to clear the room of unwanted smoke or odors, the reverse blade rotation switch featured on all well-made ceiling fans is most useful.

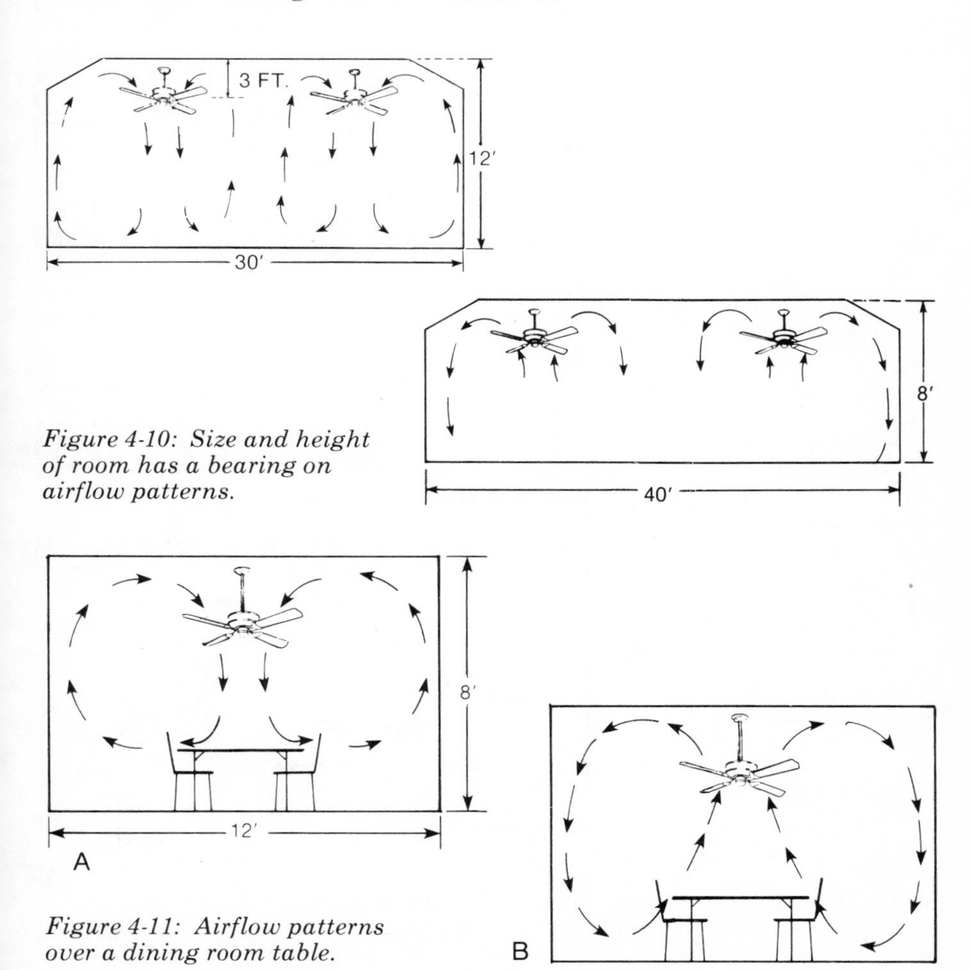

Figure 4-10: Size and height of room has a bearing on airflow patterns.

Figure 4-11: Airflow patterns over a dining room table.

LOCATION

Typical room locations for ceiling fans in one- and two-story houses and a one-bedroom apartment are illustrated in Figure 4-12. As you will note, ceiling fans can be installed in almost any area of the home where sleeping, eating, playing, working, and other household activities take

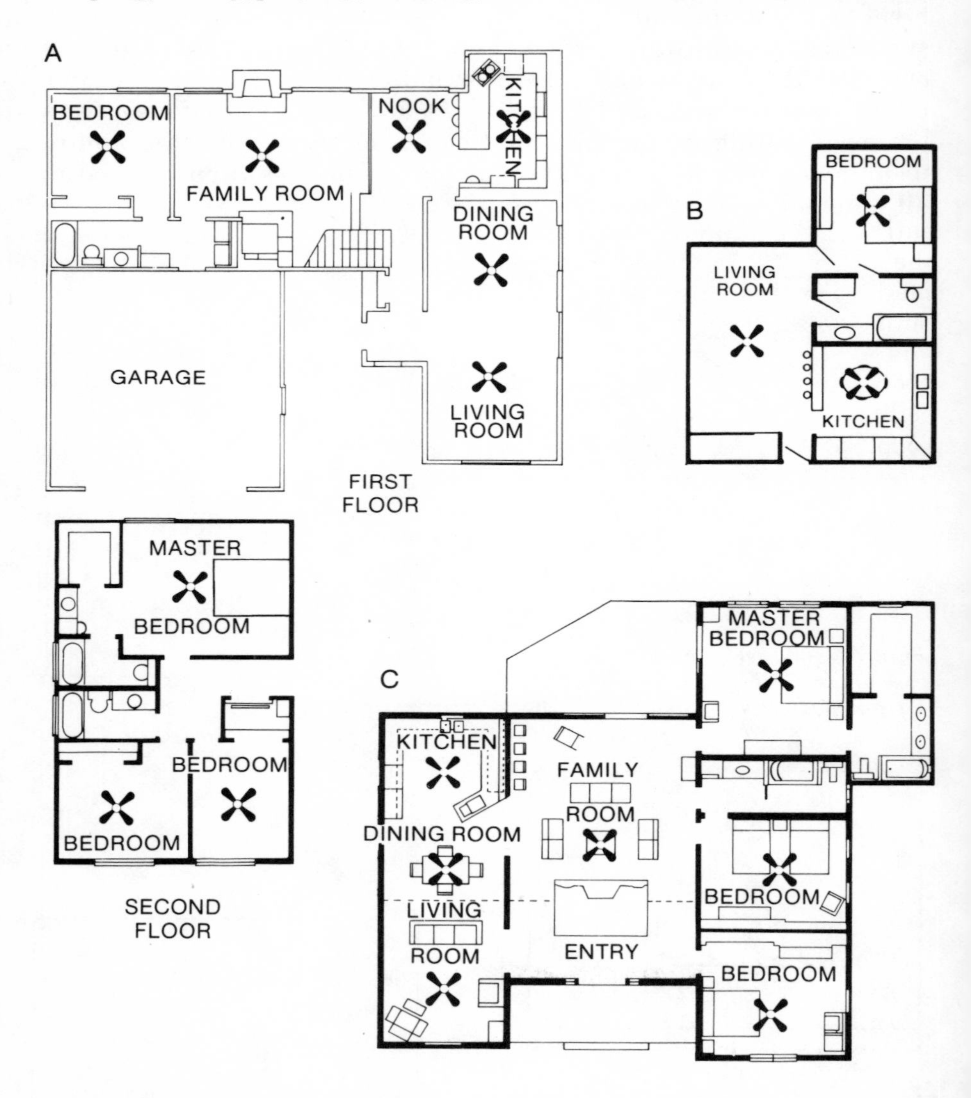

Figure 4-12: Locations of ceiling fans in (A) a two-story house, (B) a one-bedroom apartment, and (C) a one-story house.

place. In large rooms, you may wish to install two fans; while in other areas, small fans or even no fans are suggested to give overall household comfort. The installation of a multiple fan system such as those illustrated here will, in the long run, save additional money by cutting down heating and cooling expenses. In other words, as previously stated, a multiple fan system in your home will soon pay for itself and will give full comfort to your family. Also, keep in mind that the placement of fans outdoors on porches, patios, and near pools can be particularly useful for cooling and in keeping insects at bay.

When installing a ceiling fan in a bedroom, the ideal location is over the foot of the bed (Figure 4-13). If this isn't possible, placement off to either side of the bed is suggested. **Never** locate the fan directly over the head of the bed. In the kitchen most fans are best installed over the eating area and away from the stove. Also, do not position the fan above the path of a swinging door. Remember, for safety reasons, the fan blades must be at least 7′ from the floor. Therefore, the minimum recommended ceiling height from which the fan should be mounted is 8′. If you wish to include lights in your fan installation (Figure 4-14), the problem of less than minimal clearance can be solved by placing the ceiling fan over a table, bed, or some other piece of furniture. By doing so, people won't be able to walk directly under the fan (Figure 4-15). As long as the fan blades are at least 7′ from the floor, it will work properly and there shouldn't be any overhead problem.

Figure 4-13: In a bedroom, it is best to place the ceiling fan at the foot of the bed.

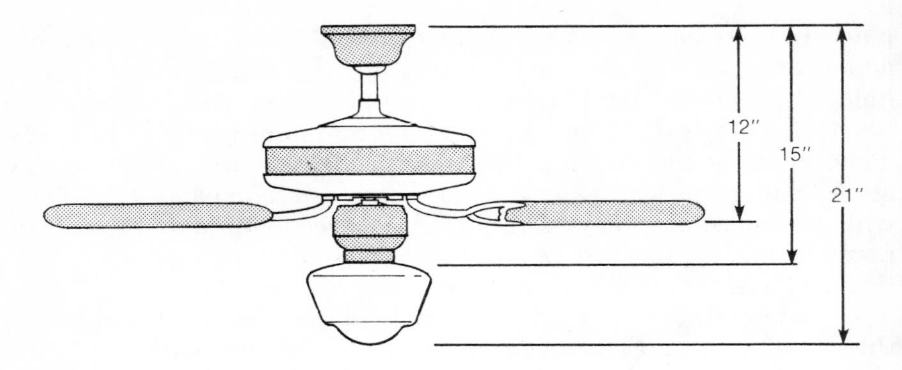

Figure 4-14: Dimensions of typical fan and light kit setup.

Figure 4-15: A table under the light fixture solves many height problems.

A few manufacturers produce so-called "low-profile" light kits that can be mounted on an 8′ ceiling fan and still have room for most people to walk under. They usually have a clearance of 6′ 7″. Of course, there are fans on the market that require greater ceiling heights for both appearance and safety (Figure 4-16).

Figure 4-16: Some fans, such as the model shown here, look best on high ceilings.

In any ceiling fan installation, the tips of blades should be no closer than 18″ to the wall in order to provide sufficient clearance for the fan blades. If space permits, even greater clearance is recommended for optimum air circulation.

Before leaving the subject of the decorative values of the standard ceiling fans for residential locations, it might be interesting to look at some other types of ceiling fan systems available for commercial use. Whether it be a restaurant or grand dining salon, an office, or retail center—anywhere an added atmosphere is needed—spectacular ceiling fan systems such as shown in Figure 4-17 can be employed.

There are three basic types of unique fan systems in use today. They are:

- **The Belt Driven System** (Figure 4-17A). All fans are powered via leather-styled belts connected to one centrally located motor, offering the finest in ambiance and animated visual quality.
- **The Paddlewheel System** (Figure 4-17B). Large hand-sewn palm blades from the Philippines grace brass bars on a different, horizontal rotating device.
- **The Oscillating Fan System** (Figure 4-17C). Beautiful blades gracefully and quietly move forward and backward, intimating cool breezes of enchanting adventure.

A

B

Figure 4-17: Three unique ceiling fan systems suitable for commercial applications where atmosphere is important. Installations of these types are not covered in this book.

C

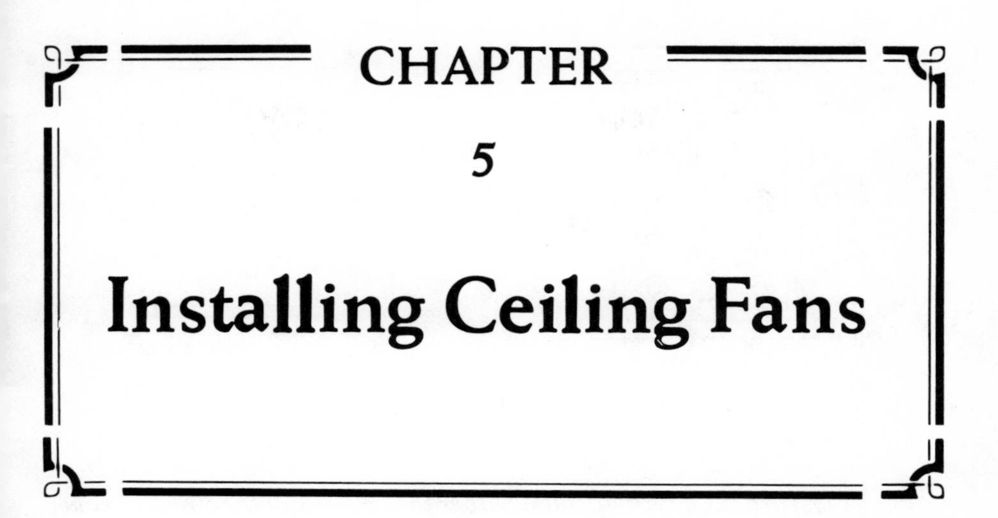

CHAPTER 5

Installing Ceiling Fans

Although the modern ceiling fan is a fairly simple device, installation varies in its degree of difficulty depending on where it's installed. Each manufacturer packages instructions for their fans. Be sure to follow the instructions carefully. Here are some added suggestions for mounting ceiling fans. Read them carefully before installing any ceiling fan.

SAFETY FIRST

Safety and the proper operation of your ceiling fan are both dependent on a thorough knowledge of the unit and proper installation; therefore, before attempting to install and operate your ceiling fan, read your owner's manual completely and very carefully. Retain your owner's manual for future reference. Also read the following safety tips and keep them in mind when installing any ceiling fan:

- To avoid the possibility of electrical shock, be certain that the electricity is turned off at the fuse box or circuit breaker (Figure 5-1) before removing an existing light fixture or wiring the fan.
- All wiring must be in accordance with national and local electrical codes.
- The ceiling fan must be grounded as a precaution against electrical shock.
- Remember that your ceiling fan requires a grounded electrical supply of 120 volts AC, 60 hertz, and a 15 ampere circuit (minimum). Maximum current requirement for the fan with lights is 4 amperes.

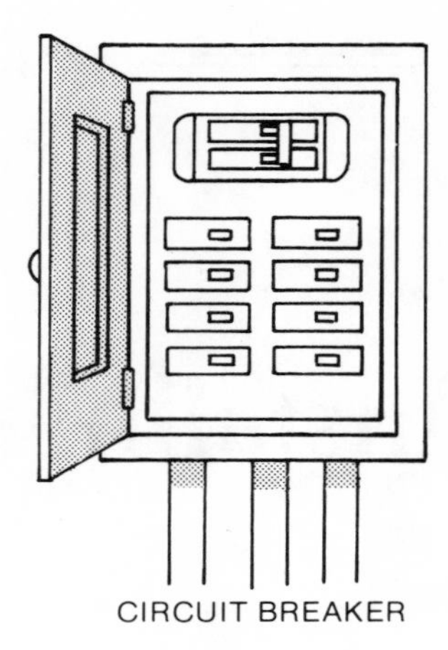

Figure 5-1: Turn the electricity off at either the fuse box or the circuit breaker before attempting any installation work.

• Always follow the recommended instructions for the proper method of wiring your ceiling fan. If you feel you don't have enough electrical wiring knowledge or experience, refer to a do-it-yourself wiring handbook or have the fan installed by a licensed electrician.

• When installing your ceiling fan to an existing light fixture outlet box, first check to be sure that the outlet box is securely anchored to the ceiling. The crossbar or "J" hook must be supported by one of the methods explained later in the chapter. The outlet box and joist must be capable of firmly supporting at least 50 pounds to provide a safety margin.

• If your ceiling doesn't have an electrical box installed or the proper wiring isn't available, you may wish to contact a certified or licensed electrician for installation.

• Never install a fan in an area where there is a possibility of getting it wet or where high humidity can cause condensation on metal parts.

• Where wire nuts are employed, make sure all bare wires are within the connectors. When installing the canopy hatch, make sure all wires are within the canopy and that it does not pinch any of the wires.

• The distance from the tip of the fan to the wall (Figure 5-2) should be a minimum of 18″.

• The fan must be mounted with the blades at least 7′ from the floor to minimize the possibility of accidental contact with the fan blades. This is true regardless of ceiling height.

• The hanger stem assembly supplied with your kit provides proper floor clearance and mounting strength for a standard 8′ ceiling instal-

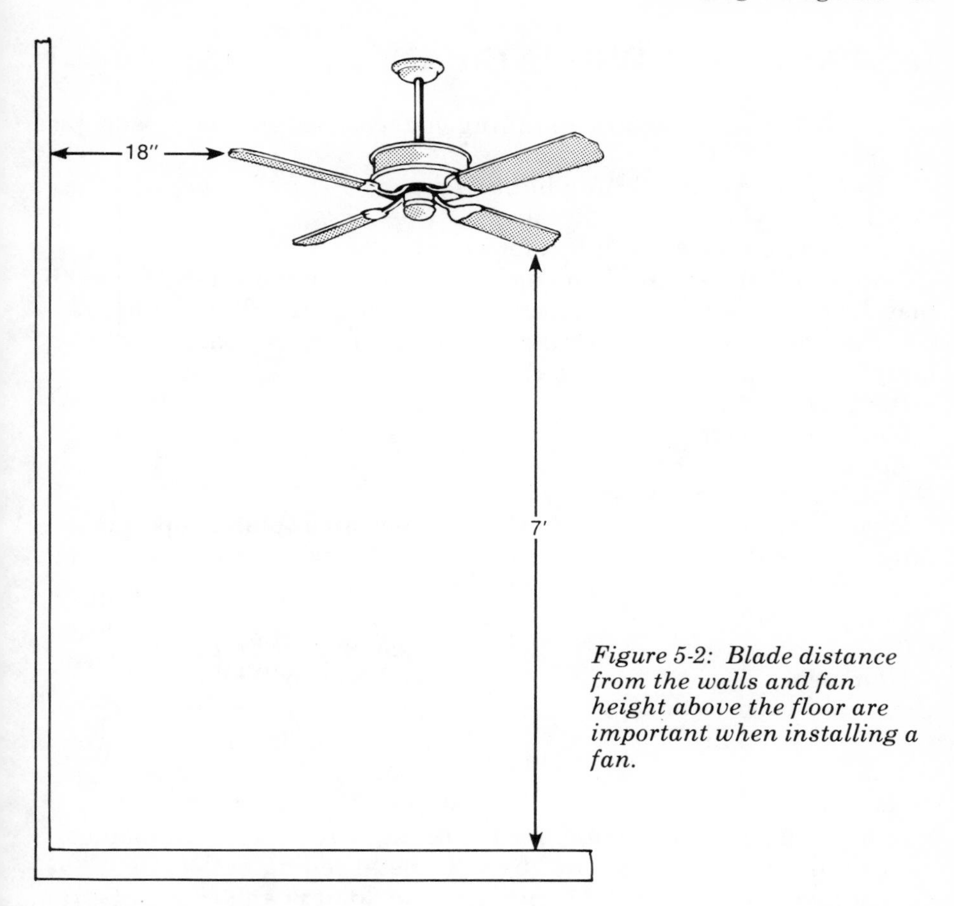

Figure 5-2: Blade distance from the walls and fan height above the floor are important when installing a fan.

lation. Extra length poles are available from your local dealer for higher ceiling applications requiring increased length.

• When using an extension pole, make certain that the two nuts at the top are locked against each other so that they cannot turn.

• When assembling the fan, be sure that the hanger stem is secured to the top support of the fan.

• Blades are packed as a matched set of four (or five) to assure smooth fan operation. If more than one fan is being installed, be careful not to mix blades from different cartons.

• Inspect the contents of your carton for possible shipping or handling damage and report any such damage directly to your dealer.

• Use a stepladder of adequate height and strength when mounting your fan. It is also a good idea to have a partner to steady the ladder, hand up tools and parts, etc.

INSTALLING A CEILING FAN

There are several ways of installing your ceiling fan. The most popular are:

1. Using an existing ceiling light fixture;
2. Using a ceiling fan swag kit; or
3. Installing a new outlet box for your fan.

Tools and Materials. The tools and electrical materials needed to install your ceiling fan will depend on the type of installation required. For instance, when you're hanging the fan from an existing ceiling light fixture, the only tools needed are:

Blade screwdriver | Pliers
Knife or wire strippers | Stepladder
Adjustable wrench

No wiring supplies are usually needed.

If you plan to install a new outlet for your fan or plan to operate the fan with a wall control switch rather than the traditional pull-chain, you may need the following additional equipment:

Compass saw | Lead pencil
Chisel and mallet | Electrical drill or brace
Hammer | 1/8″ and 1/4″ drill bits

Optional—needed for some types of installation:

18″ extension drill bit | Magnetic stud finder
Nail punch | 1/2″ drill bit
Hacksaw | Fish tape

Other items needed to complete the ceiling outlet for a fan include:

1. Standard 4″ by 1-1/2″ or 4″ by 1/2″ metal ceiling outlet box;
2. Sufficient three-wire BX or nonmetallic Romex cable (Figure 5-3) to connect fan to power source or electrical raceway; and
3. BX cable connectors (if BX cable is used).

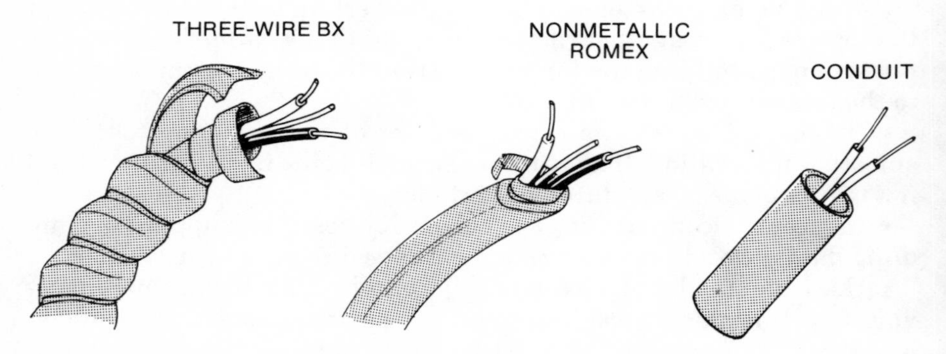

Figure 5-3: Wire types used in fan wiring.

Caution: Before touching the existing fixture, be sure to turn off the power to the line upon which you will be working. It is **not** safe just to place the wall switch in the OFF position, since the current may come to the fixture before it goes to the switch. As with all electrical work, you must first remove the fuse or throw the circuit breaker controlling the line or shut off the current to the whole house.

After the current is off, start the removal of the old fixture by loosening the screws or nuts that hold it in place. Lower the old fixture to expose the wiring and the ceiling outlet box. Then cut the fixture wires or, if solderless connectors (wire nuts) have been used, unscrew them and disconnect the wires. (Do **not** touch any other wires in the outlet box.) The fixture can now be removed.

After removing the old fixture, check the outlet box to be sure that it is securely fastened to a solid base (joist or beam). Remember that the outlet box must be capable of supporting at least 50 pounds. If the outlet box is not secure for such a load, it may be necessary to fasten it as shown and described on page 81. Also if Romex type cable was used to wire the electrical box, the presence of a third wire connected to the electrical box indicates that the box is grounded. This ground wire may be a bare wire (no insulating jacket) or a green insulated wire. The two supply wires will be white and black insulated wires.

If the wiring to the electrical box is enclosed in electrical conduit pipe, the ground wire may not be present. The conduit itself could serve as the ground. **Note:** If you're not sure if the electrical box is grounded, contact a certified electrician for advice.

Using an Existing Ceiling Fixture

The exact method of mounting a ceiling fan depends on the make. Some fans are easy to install while others can present problems. Therefore, when selecting a ceiling fan, consider the method of its mounting most carefully. We believe our CasaBlanca Hang-Tru is one of the simplest on the market to mount. Let's take a more detailed look at what's involved in using this system.

Step #1. Attach the crossbar, ground wire down, to the ceiling box with crossbar screws and washers provided with the fan (Figure 5-4A). The crossbar can be adjusted in the box by sliding the bar back and forth along the slotted openings. Gently tighten the screws. **Note:** Don't overtighten the crossbar screws. Any overtightening of the crossbar screws can cause the bar to bend, therefore creating unnecessary tension and warpage which could hinder the final assembly of the unit. Tighten the crossbar screws until they are snug; **do not overtighten.**

Step #2. Attach the canopy to the crossbar with the three canopy screws, and tighten until rigid (Figure 5-4B). Be careful not to scratch the canopy with the screwdriver. On sloped ceilings, align the canopy opening toward the top or peak of the room. A canopy installed in this manner provides full support for the ceiling fan.

Step #3. Install the pole assembly on the fan body. This assembly (Figure 5-4C) consists of a nylon ball, a cover tube, a rubber grommet, and a hanger stem. To fasten the pole assembly to the fan body, pass the ball over the hanger so that the hex head engages the hex socket in the ball. Then pass the cover tube and rubber grommet over the hanger stem. Once this is done, pass the wires from the top of the fan body through the hanger stem. Back off the lock screw. Attach the stem to the top of the fan body. Hand tighten the pole assembly by turning the ball until the rubber grommet contacts the fan body. Tighten the lock screw securely with an adjustable wrench. **Note:** It is **absolutely** imperative that the lock screw be set tightly against the threaded rod after the fan is assembled to avoid unthreading.

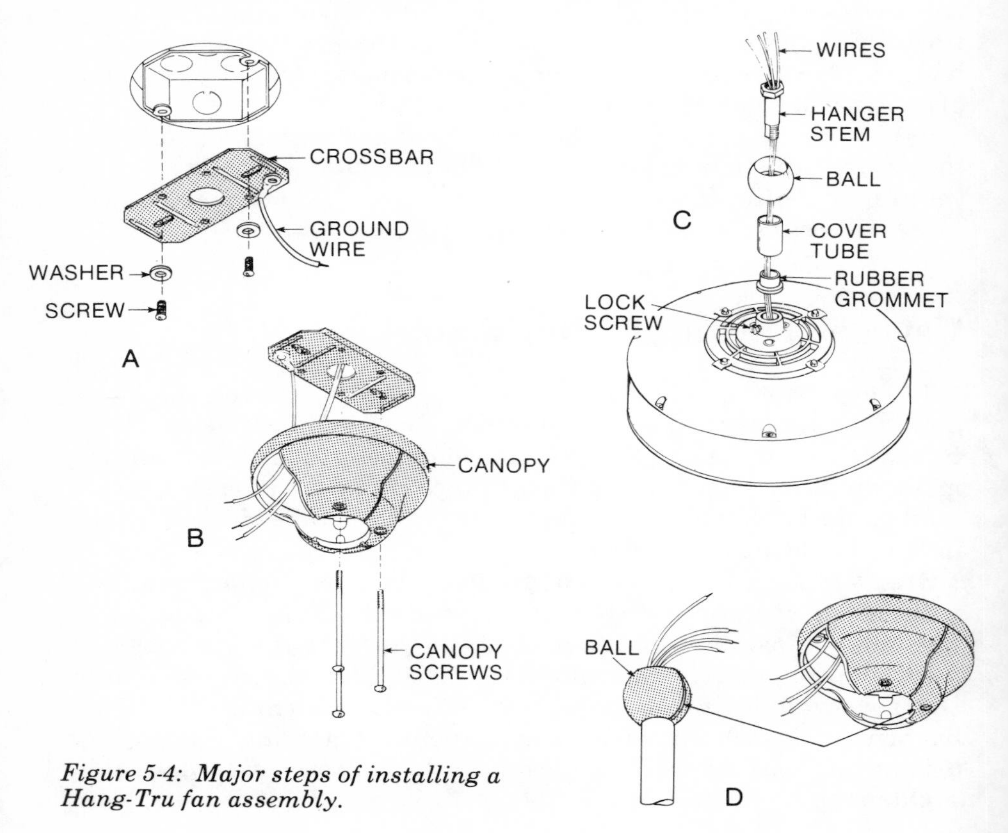

Figure 5-4: Major steps of installing a Hang-Tru fan assembly.

Step #4. To hang the fan in the canopy, hold the fan body firmly and insert the nylon ball into the canopy opening. **Note:** The pin opposite the canopy opening must fit in the slot on the nylon ball (Figure 5-4D).

Step #5. Connect the fan wires to the ceiling outlet box wires: white to white, black to colored, green to green. Cap the wires with the wire nuts provided (Figure 5-5A). When a standard assembly is employed, the wires from the fan body must be cut. A good indicator of the length of the wires which are required is the ground wire attached to the hex head on the inside of the nylon ball; that is, the length of the wires from the fan motor past the ball should correspond to the length of the ground wire. **Note:** If you're using a plastic junction or outlet box, connect the house ground wire to green ground wires and cap with wire nut.

Step #6. Tuck the wires into the canopy (Figure 5-5B) and install the canopy hatch. To insert the screwdriver to tighten the canopy screw, tilt the fan body away from the hatch opening.

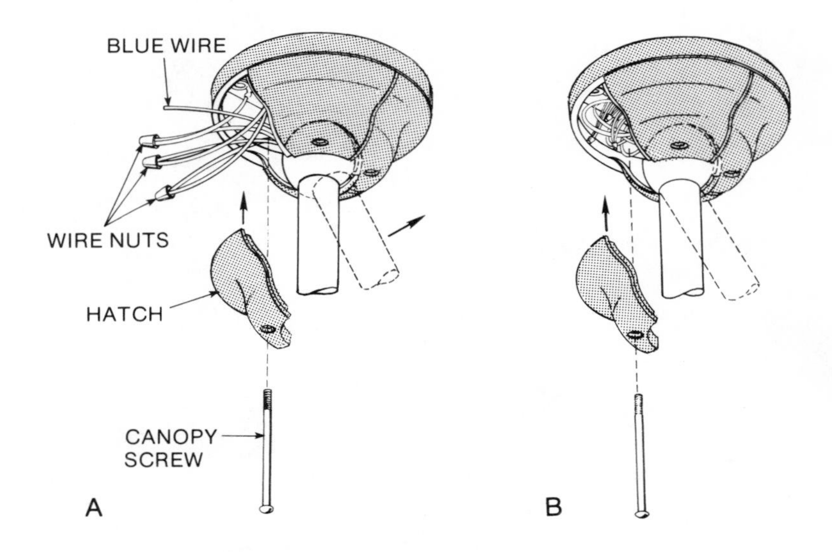

Figure 5-5: Wiring a fan to existing wiring.

Figure 5-6 shows several other methods used by fan manufacturers to mount their units. When a fan is installed on a vaulted or cathedral ceiling, some of these methods require a special "swivel" kit to be installed to permit hanging on a pitched ceiling (Figure 5-7). The CasaBlanca Hang-Tru system described earlier will hang true on any ceiling pitch without any "special" kits (Figure 5-8).

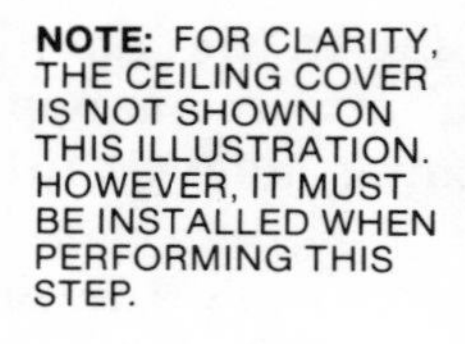

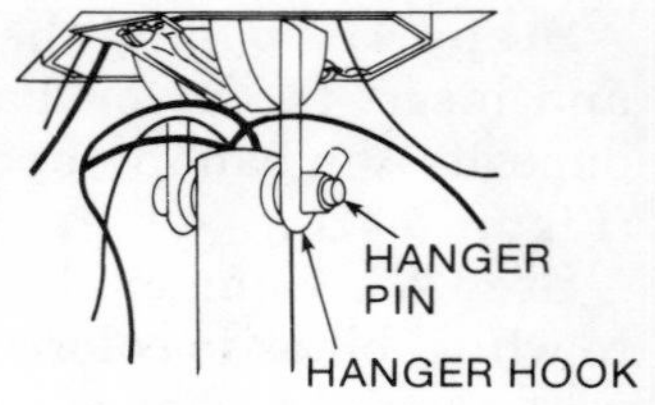

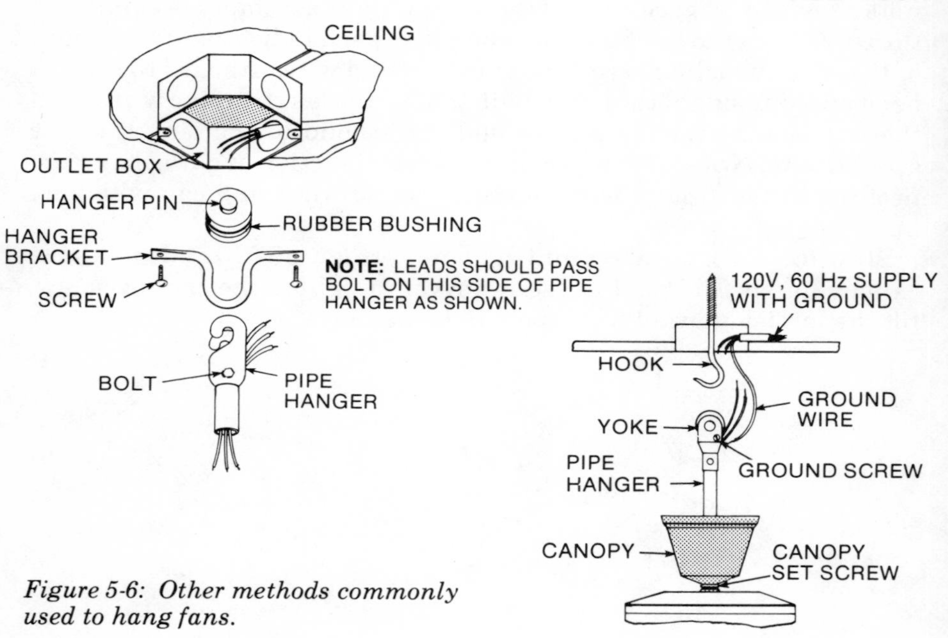

Figure 5-6: Other methods commonly used to hang fans.

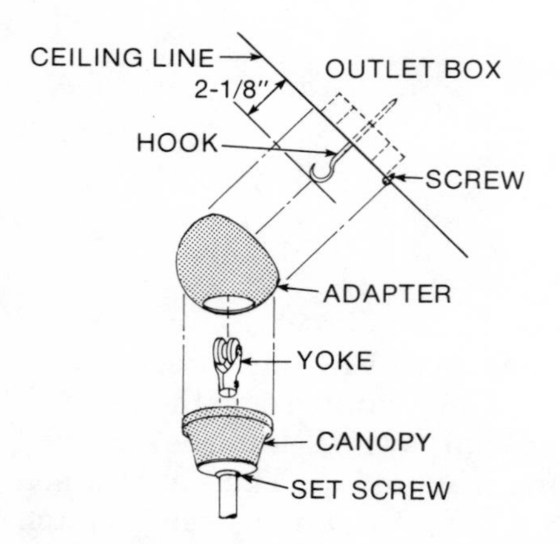

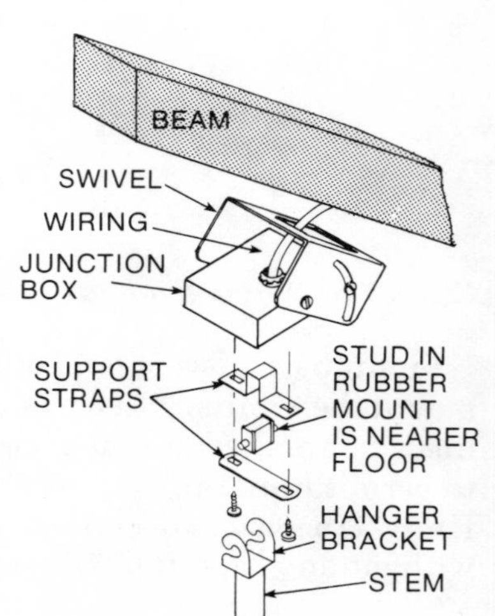

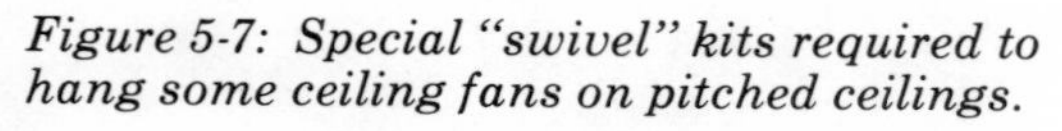
Figure 5-7: Special "swivel" kits required to hang some ceiling fans on pitched ceilings.

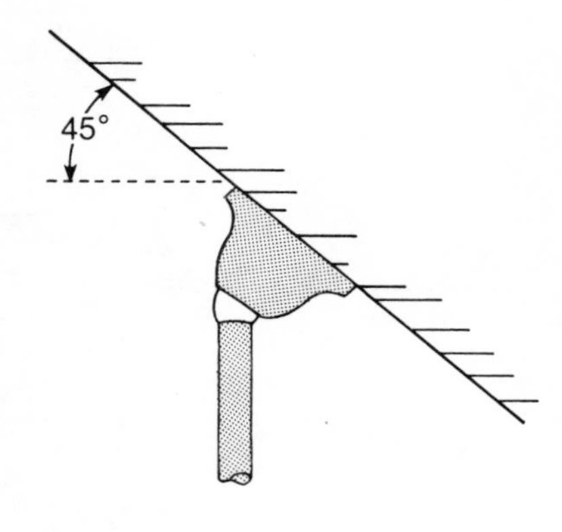

Figure 5-8: How a Hang-Tru fan hangs on a pitched ceiling.

Using a Ceiling Fan Swag Kit

If a permanent ceiling outlet is not available (and you do not wish to install a new outlet), a decorative swag kit is the answer (Figure 5-9). No interior wiring from the power source to the fan location is necessary; just plug in the swag kit's line cord to the nearest convenient wall outlet.

An outlet box must be installed to hang the fan. Notch away the plaster or ceiling board to the size of a **shallow** outlet box, using either a keyhole saw or chisel and mallet. Secure the outlet box to the joist or beam using the wood screws provided with your fan. But before making the cutout in the ceiling, check to make sure that the location is within reach of a convenient wall outlet (Figure 5-10). **Note:** This swag kit shouldn't be installed on radiant-heated ceilings.

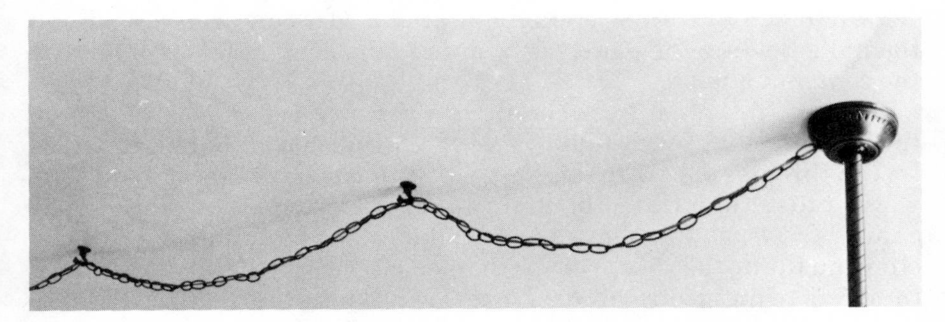

Figure 5-9: A swag kit with 15' of decorative chain and 18' of wire can be used for fast installation anywhere without permanent ceiling wiring.

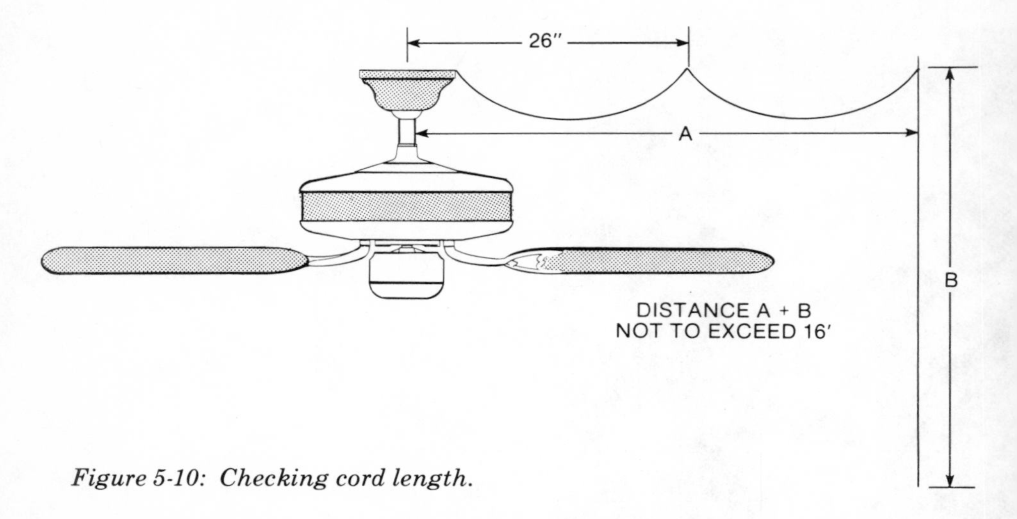

Figure 5-10: Checking cord length.

Before hanging the fan, be sure to punch out the knockout slot at the top of the canopy, using a nail punch or similar tool. Then proceed to install the fan as described in the owner's manual or previously in this book. Once this is completed, the swag hooks can be installed.

Select and mark the location for the swag hooks. Locate one hook close to the wall and the second between the first hook and the fan to keep the cord from interfering with the fan blades. Drill a 1/8″ pilot hole into the beam or joist and screw the hook in firmly (Figure 5-11).

To find the beams or joists in a plastered or wallboard ceiling, use one of the following methods:

1. Tap the ceiling lightly with your fist. A hollow sound means there is no joist. A solid sound indicates the presence of a joist.
2. Measure from the corner. Joists are generally located either 16″ or 24″ apart, depending on local building codes. Try measuring out from the corner of a room to find the approximate location of a joist; then use the tapping technique to confirm joist locations.
3. On drywall ceilings, a magnetic stud finder can be used to detect the nails holding the panels or boards to the joists. This will indicate the center of a joist.

To assemble the cord and chain, start at the end of the electrical cord, thread it through every four or five chain links until the entire cord is woven through the chain. Leave about 8″ of slack wire at the end to be wired into the fan. Hang the chain on the hooks, making sure the swag chain is at least 10″ above the fan blades. When hanging the swag chain on the hooks, do not drape the electric wire on the hooks or fasten the chain to the electrical box. **Note:** Do **not** plug the cord into the electrical wall outlet until after the installation has been completed.

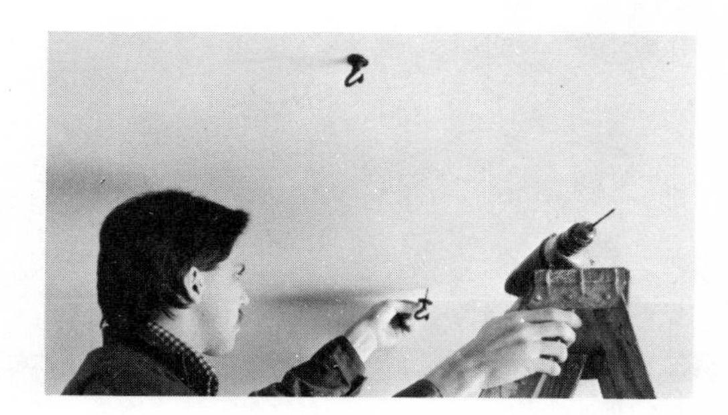

Figure 5-11: Hanging the hooks and their locations.

To make the electrical connection, run the wires through the canopy knockout and connect them with the fan body wires: white to white, black to colored. (The third wire, usually blue in color, isn't for fan use only.) Cap the connections with three wire nuts. Tuck the wires into the canopy and install the hatch, using a canopy screw. To insert the screwdriver, tilt the fan away from the hatch opening.

The installation is now ready for the blades. See page 88 for details on how to install ceiling fan blades.

Installing a New Outlet for Your Fan

If you don't have an existing fixture located where you wish to place your fan, a new ceiling junction box must be installed and an electric cable run to it. It is recommended that this work be done by a qualified or licensed electrician. However, if you feel confident that you can do the job, and local electrical code permits, proceed as follows:

New Construction. In new construction, or in cases where the joists are accessible from above (such as an open attic floor), the wire is run between the ceiling fan and the power source through the ceiling joists (Figure 5-12) or parallel to the joists. (In the latter method, fasten the cable against the joists with wire staples.) To get the wire below to the power source, it may be necessary to drill a hole down through the header (Figure 5-13). The wire can then be run down between the studs to the power source.

Old Construction. The first step in old construction work is to determine where the cable—either BX or nonmetallic—will run (generally parallel to the joists) from the fan unit to a power source. Although the fan could be connected directly to the main power box (circuit breaker or fuse box), it might be easier to add the wiring from another receptacle or outlet box (unless this source is already at maximum capacity). Before tying in at a junction box, always trace the electrical cables lead-

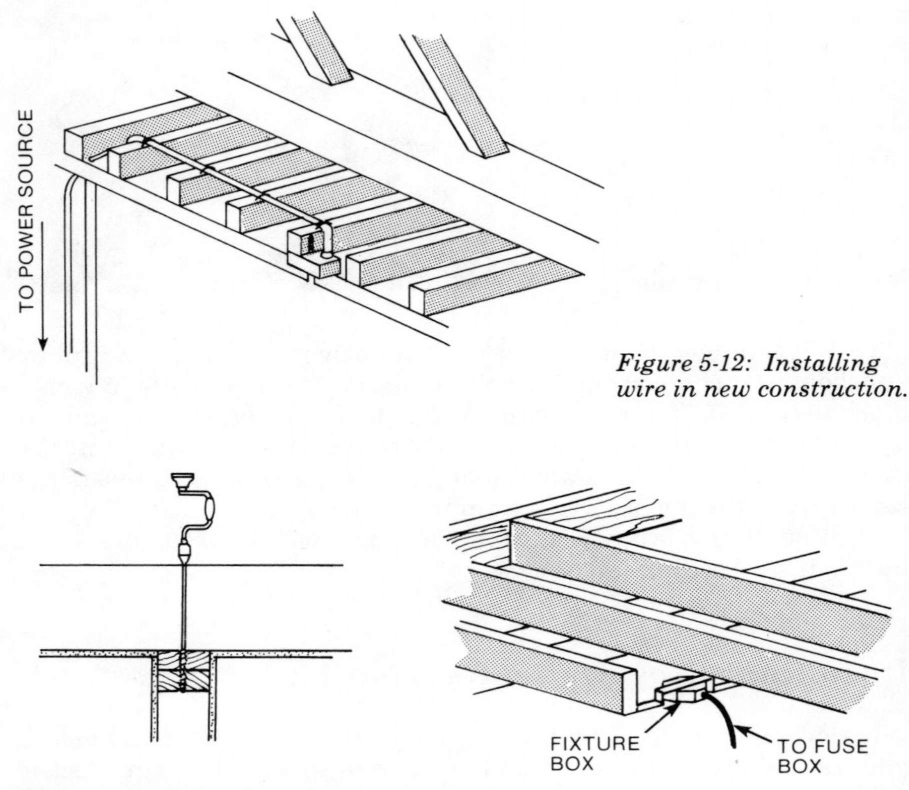

Figure 5-12: Installing wire in new construction.

Figure 5-13: Drilling through a header.

ing to the power box for a check of the voltage. Be sure you are not connecting 240-volt outlet wiring to your 120-volt fan.

To determine the amount of wire cable needed, measure the distance across the ceiling from the fan to the wall and down to the power source. Then, to this figure, add three additional feet to get the total amount of wire needed.

Once you've determined the location for the fan, use a pencil to outline the area that must be cut out of the ceiling. Use the outlet box as a pattern. Drill 1/4″ holes through the plaster or drywall into the hollow part of the ceiling at the corners of your outline. Starting at the drilled holes, cut away the plaster or drywall along the lines of your outline, using a keyhole or saber saw. Once the cutout has been completed, you are ready to run your wire from the opening to the power source.

In an existing house, it is usually necessary to "fish" the wire through the spaces between the ceilings and walls. This is best done with a fish tape—a tempered flat steel wire (1/16″ by 1/8″) that comes in coils of 50′, 75′, and 100′. Ordinary steel baling wire can be used in some "fishing" jobs through enclosed areas, though it does not have the springy temper and stiffness necessary to straighten out the tape when it hits an obstruction.

The method of fishing wires will be determined by existing conditions. To run a wire from the ceiling fan to a power source in cases when there is a room or attic above, remove the baseboard and drill diagonally through the supporting beams into the wall cavity. Use a brace and 18″ bit, or an electric drill and an electrician's bit (Figure 5-14).

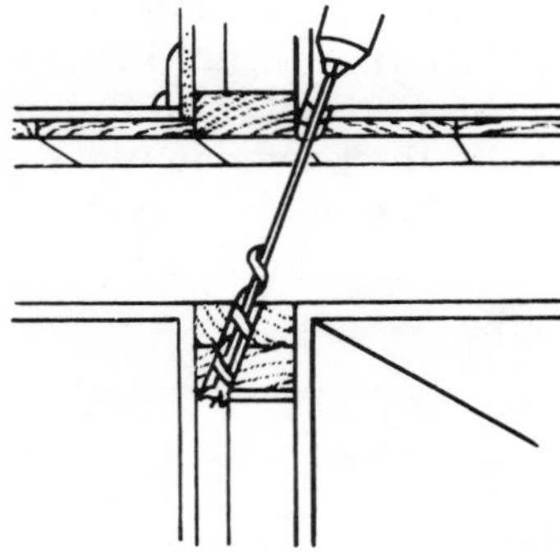

Figure 5-14: Drilling through from upstairs.

"Snake" a short length of fish tape down through the floorboard hole and header hole from the second floor and bring the end out at the power source. (If the cable is to be run down into the basement, it is necessary to drill a hole between two floor joists through the plate on which the wall rests [Figure 5-15].) Push a longer fish tape through the ceiling

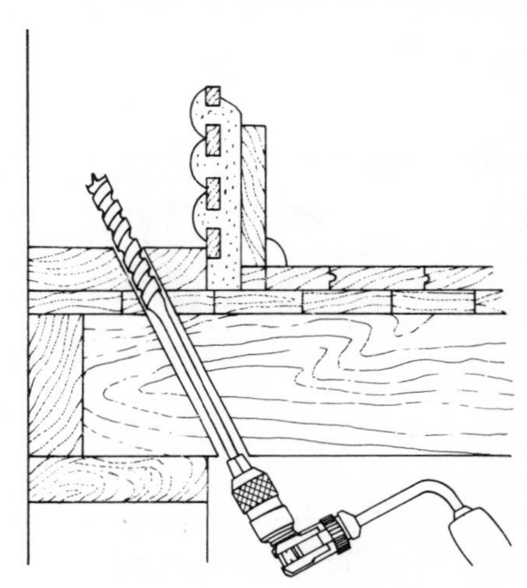

Figure 5-15: Drilling through plate from the basement.

hole and hook the first tape (Figure 5-16A). Draw the short fish tape or wire down and pull the long one through into the room (Figure 5-16B). The electrical cable is attached to the hook on the fish tape, then pulled through the ceiling and wall.

If there is no access above, cut a hole in the wall 5″ from the ceiling. Bore diagonally up through the header into the ceiling cavity. Insert the short tape or wire into the cavity (Figure 5-17A). Then, insert a second tape through the fan hole. Fish until the tapes interlock (Figure 5-17B). Withdraw the tapes through the ceiling hole until the hook of the wall tape can be grasped. Attach the cable to the tape hook, then pull the tape and the cable through the ceiling cavity and down the wall. As you do, feed the free end of the tape down and out through the power source outlet (Figure 5-17C). Patch the wall hole and finish it.

Do **not** make any electrical connections to the power source as yet. First, install the ceiling outlet box for the fan. This can be accomplished

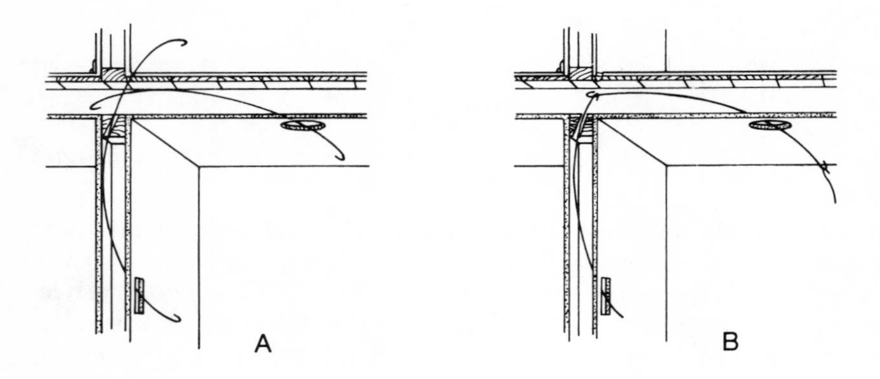

Figure 5-16: "Fishing" the wire through with room above.

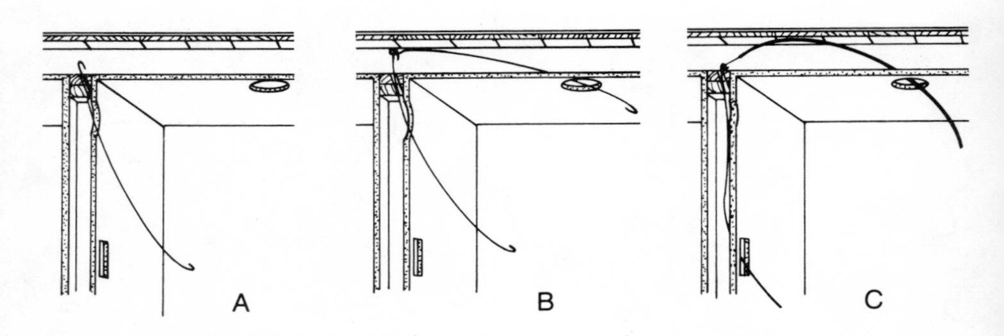

Figure 5-17: "Fishing" the wire through where there is no access.

in several ways, depending on the space available and type of ceiling you have.

1. With the lath and plaster ceiling, a **shallow** outlet or junction box can be supported by a special metal hanger designed for this purpose (Figure 5-18A). Remove the locknut from the hanger's threaded stud. Insert and center the hanger in the opening. Fasten the electrical cable to the junction box. Pass the threaded stud through the center knockout in the box and secure with the locknut (Figure 5-18B).

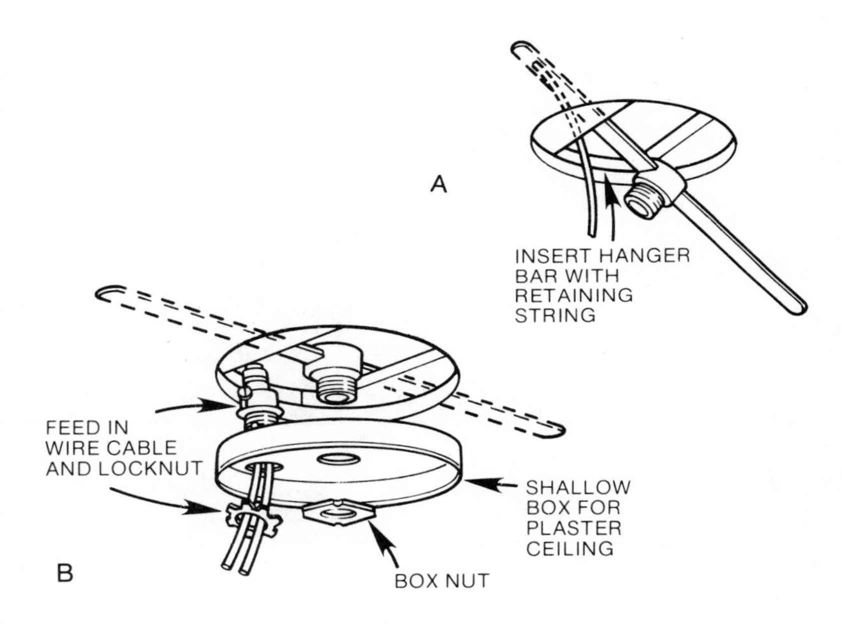

Figure 5-18: Installing an electrical box in a lath and plaster ceiling.

2. Where space is available from the top, a 2″ by 4″ board can be installed between the joists as shown in Figure 5-19. Nail the wood piece securely between the joists. Then remove one of the side knockouts from a 4″ octagon electrical outlet box and secure it to the wood piece so that the box is flush with the ceiling. Pull the wire down through the knockout.

3. As shown in Figure 5-20, a wood block can be installed at the side of the joists. Before securing the outlet box to the block, remove one of the knockouts from the 4″ octagon electrical box so that the wire can be run through the box before it has been installed.

4. When a **shallow** or low profile electrical box is used, the ceiling outlet box can be installed directly on the joists as shown in Figure 5-21. The wire should be pushed through the box before it is fastened. Inci-

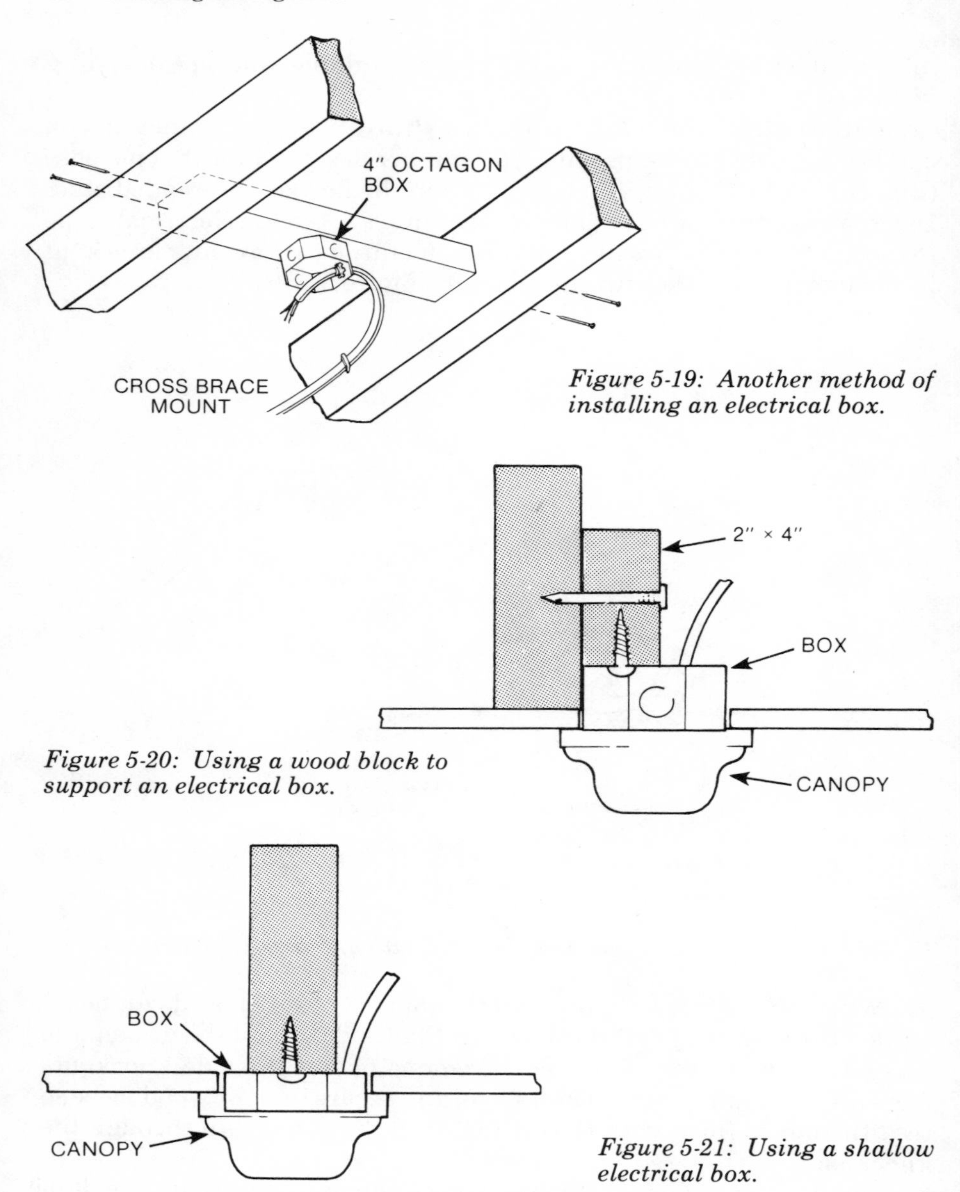

Figure 5-19: Another method of installing an electrical box.

Figure 5-20: Using a wood block to support an electrical box.

Figure 5-21: Using a shallow electrical box.

dentally, some manufacturers make available a ceiling adapter that can be used with a standard canopy to mask an oversized ceiling hole (Figure 5-22). **Note:** All four methods can be used to reinforce an existing electrical outlet box.

Once the outlet box has been installed, the ceiling fan can be installed and wired. Turn off the electricity at the fuse box or circuit

Figure 5-22: Ceiling adapters can be used to mask oversized holes.

breaker and wire the fan to its power source. Figure 5-23 illustrates two methods for making the connections. Optional wiring methods are given in Chapter 7.

Metal Raceway. If you are unable to run cable through the walls (with an exposed wood and beam ceiling, for instance), another option is to run it along the surface through a metal raceway (Figure 5-24). Raceway comes in 5′ and 10′ lengths, consisting of back and front sections, which are cut to desired lengths with a hacksaw. The back half is screwed to the wall. Three separate wires (black, white, and green), not cable, are laid in to carry current and to provide a ground; the front half of the raceway is snapped on. Small snap-on fittings protect all the joints.

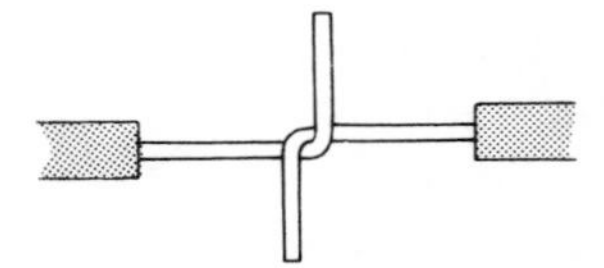

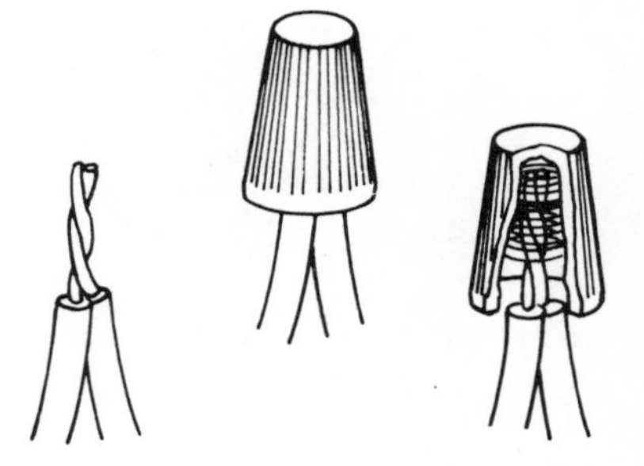

Figure 5-23: Making the electrical connections.

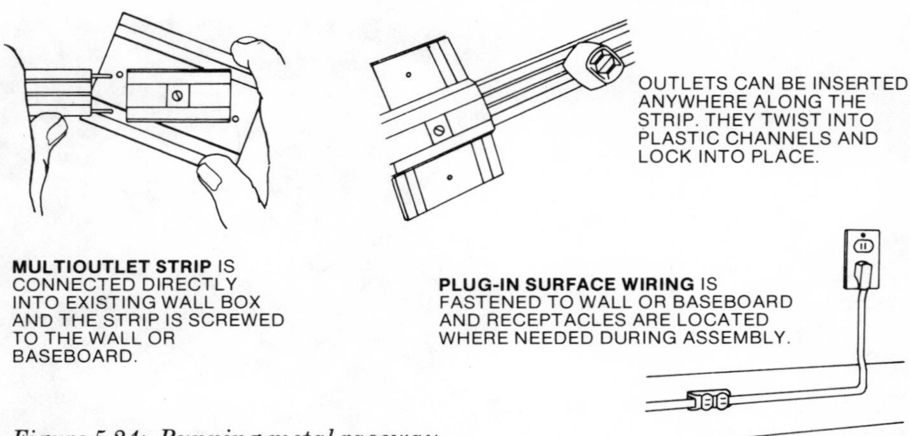

Figure 5-24: Running metal raceway.

To connect a raceway to an existing receptacle (Figure 5-25), disconnect the receptacle and attach a notched raceway plate. Bring all the house wires from the receptacle and the raceway wires through a raceway extension plate, then attach the extension plate. Attach both the house and raceway wires to the house convenience outlet receptacle. Figure 5-26 shows how the connection is made at the ceiling outlet box.

Once the outlet box is installed, the crossbar can be fastened in place and the fan can be hung and wired as previously described on page 71 or as per the manufacturer's owner's manual. When making the raceway connections at the convenience outlet receptacle and at the fan, **be sure that the power is turned off** at the fuse box or circuit breaker.

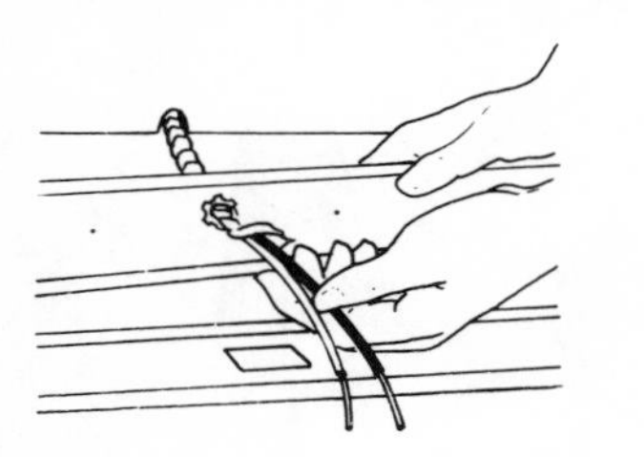

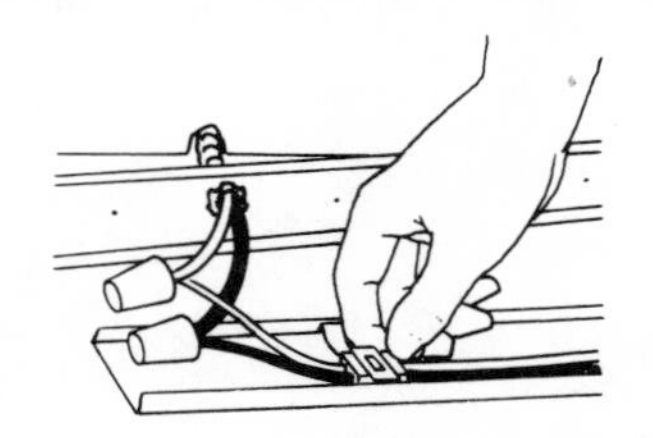

METAL RACEWAY IS FED BY BX CABLE FROM HOUSEHOLD WIRING. BASE OF RACEWAY IS FASTENED TO THE WALL OR BASEBOARD.

WIRES FROM BX CABLE ARE CONNECTED TO RACEWAY WIRING WITH WIRE NUTS. OUTLETS ARE HELD IN COVER OPENINGS BY SPRING CLIPS.

METAL RACEWAYS CAN BE FITTED WITH ADAPTER PLATES THAT PERMIT 2-WIRE CHANNELS TO BE CONNECTED WITH WALL SWITCHES.

Figure 5-25: Wiring an existing receptacle with metal raceway.

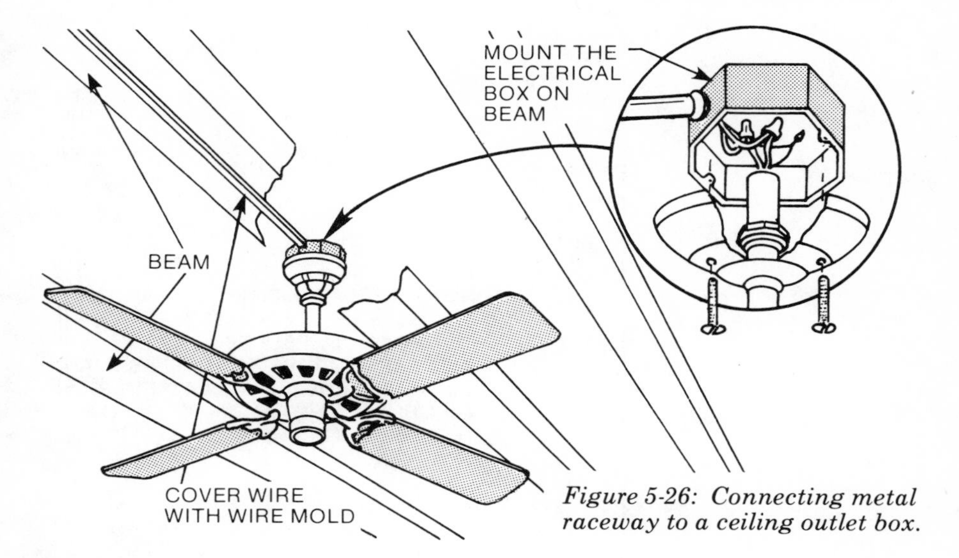

Figure 5-26: Connecting metal raceway to a ceiling outlet box.

Hanger Pole Accessories

In some locations it may be necessary to hang your CasaBlanca fan at a greater distance from the ceiling than the standard hanger pole permits. Slanted ceilings, for instance, usually require the use of longer hanger pole assemblies due to the fan blade clearance problems encountered. Higher ceilings also need lengthier hanger pole sections to either satisfy lighting requirements, if the light assembly is used, or to achieve aesthetic balance in the room.

If you are uncertain as to which length of hanger pole is required for your own personal circumstances, a guide is provided in the chart shown in Figure 5-27.

Figure 5-28 details the important factors involved in the selection of the proper hanger pole length. In this illustration, **H** equals the height of the ceiling, **T** equals the desired blade height above the floor, **S** equals the desired added drop, and **A** equals the actual distance between the bottom of the fan blade and the top of the fan canopy before any hanger pole accessories are added. **Note:** Since the exact value of **A** varies among fan models, the manufacturer's specification sheet should be consulted.

1. Add **T** (in inches) to dimension **A** for your fan model.
2. Subtract this number from **H** (in inches). This gives the added drop desired **(S)**.
3. Most accessory poles come in 6″ increments. Select the closest pole from the chart (Figure 5-27). **Note:** If the pole selected would place the blade height **T** below 7′, select the next shortest pole.

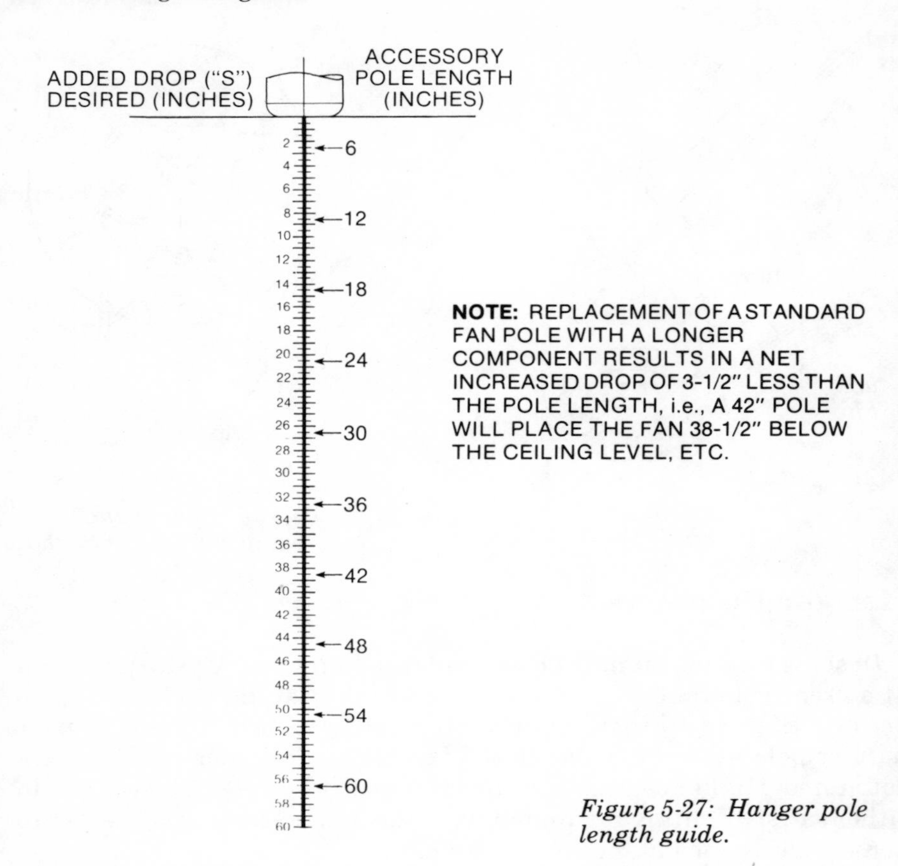

Figure 5-27: Hanger pole length guide.

As mentioned, accessory poles furnished by leading fan manufacturers are available in 6″ increments up to 60″ in length. Poles longer than 60″ are usually available by special order. Also available is a zero length down rod which permits mounting the fan as close to the ceiling as possible. **Note**: Whenever substituting aftermarket accessories for those provided with the fan, remember to consider how the alternate component will affect wall clearance, head clearance, and other factors which may lead to operating or safety hazards.

Examples. The following are examples of hanger pole length calculations. Using the Zephyr Model 1000 (Figure 5-29A):

1. For Zephyr Model 1000, **A** = 12″, so **T** + **A** = 96″ + 12″ = 108″.
2. **S** = **H** - 108″ = 120″ - 108″ = 12″ (added drop desired).
3. From Figure 5-27, an 18″ accessory pole will produce an added drop of 14-1/2″, the closest increment to the desired drop of 12″. So, **T** = **H** - **A** - **S** = 120″ - 12″ - 14-1/2″ = 93-1/2″ (actual measurement).
4. If this is too low, use the next shortest pole, 12″. This will make the

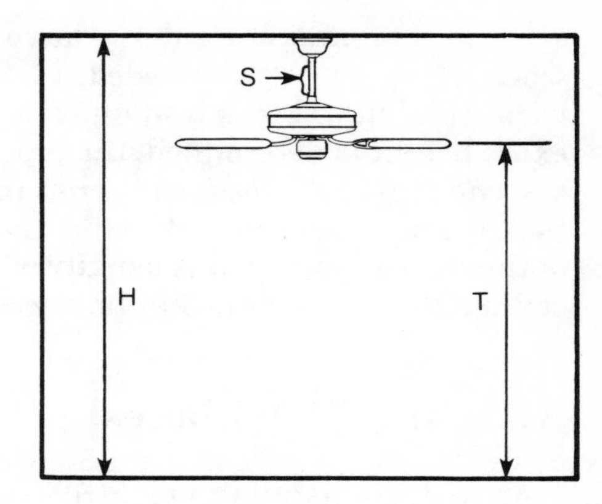

Figure 5-28: Important dimensions that help determine pole length.

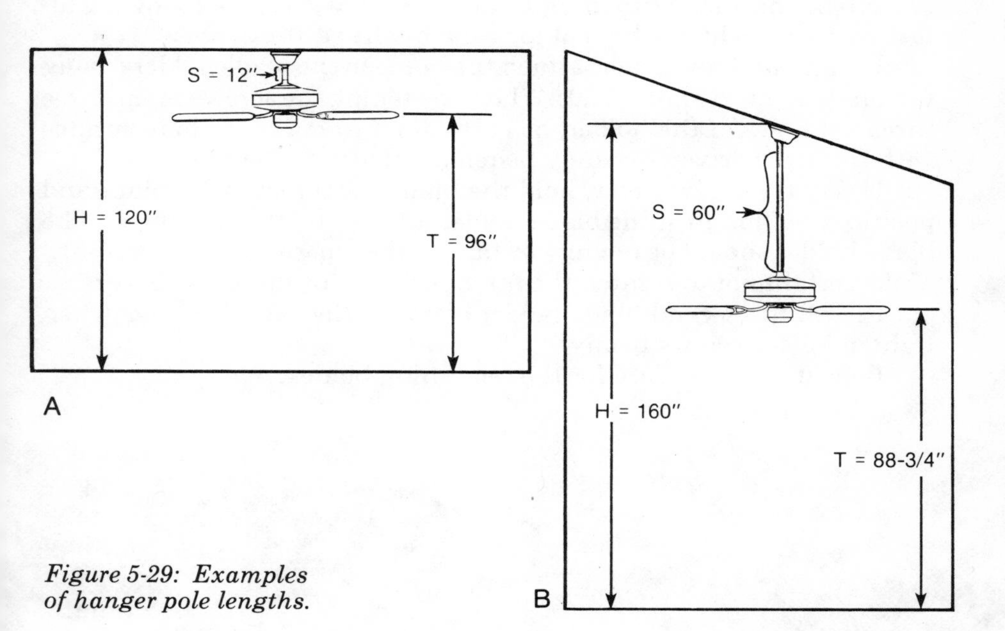

Figure 5-29: Examples of hanger pole lengths.

actual blade height **T** = 120″ - 12″ - 8-1/2″ = 99-1/2″ (actual measurement).

Using the Delta Series 10,000 (Figure 5-29B):

1. For Delta Series 10,000, **A** = 11-1/4″, so **T** + **A** = 88-3/4″ + 11-1/4″ = 100″.
2. **S** = **H** - 100″ = 160″ - 100″ = 60″ (added drop desired).
3. From Figure 5-27, it can be seen that an accessory pole greater than 60″ in length is needed to produce the 60″ added drop. Such a piece must be custom-made.

Some manufacturers don't have hanger pipe available and thus when a longer length is needed, a 1/2" diameter pipe (such as rigid electrical conduit or black iron pipe) must be used as a fan pole. After the exact height is determined, the pipe is cut to size with a hacksaw and one end must be threaded to screw into the fan motor housing. In addition, it's necessary to make other modifications in the ceiling. Because of the work involved, it is usually wise, when selecting a fan for a high ceiling, to select a unit that has accessory hanger poles available.

Attaching Fan Blades

As with all installation instructions, always follow the manufacturer's directions when attaching fan blades. However, the following attachment procedure is typical for most quality ceiling fans:

1. Using the screwdriver, attach the blade to the blade holders using fan blade screws (Figure 5-30). When tightening the screws in the three threaded holes of the holder, be careful not to mar the blade surface with the screwdriver. Securely fasten all blades to their holders.
2. Using the screwdriver, hold the blade holder screw in place and position the flange of the blade holder against the fan flywheel. (The blade holder should be facing you during this operation—Figure 5-31.) Make certain not to scratch the fan housing with the screwdriver.
3. Install the second blade holder screw in the same manner. Then tighten holder screws firmly.
4. Repeat the procedure for the remaining blades.

Figure 5-30: Attaching the blade to the blade holder.

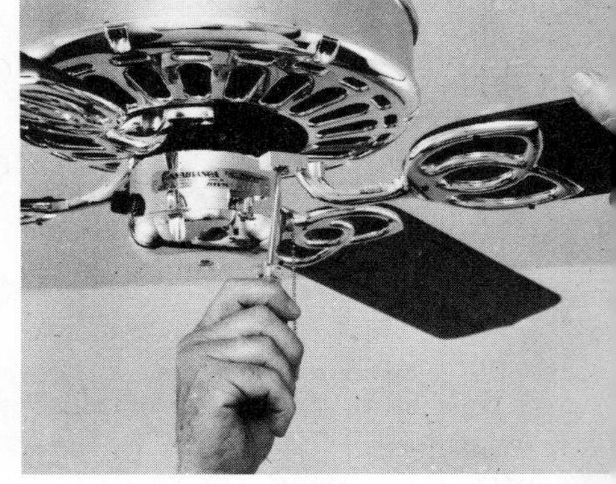

Figure 5-31: Attaching the blade holders to the flywheel.

CHAPTER 6

Use and Maintenance of Ceiling Fans

The operation of your ceiling fan depends on the manufacturer, model, and whether or not the fan has a light kit installed. Another determining operational factor is whether the controls are mounted in the traditional manner—on the fan—or are located on the wall as described in Chapter 7. In this chapter, we'll concern ourselves basically with the controls mounted on the fan.

As noted in Chapter 3, fan operation may involve three controls, two controls, or a single control. Three-control models (Figure 6-1) usually have a pull-chain mode selector switch, variable speed control, and blade reversing switch.

• The pull-chain switch selects the mode of operation of the fan. With no light kit, it operates as an ON-OFF switch:

pull, fan ON
pull again, fan OFF.

With a light kit installed, the pull-chain switch has four positions:

1. pull, fan ON
2. pull again, lights ON
3. pull again, fan and lights ON
4. pull again, both OFF.

• The variable speed control changes the speed of the fan from very slow to fast. Rotate the knob clockwise to increase the fan speed. The continuously variable speed control allows you to "fine-tune" the fan to the exact airflow desired. The setting is best determined by experimentation. It is usually not necessary to change the setting except when changing the airflow pattern (see page 59).

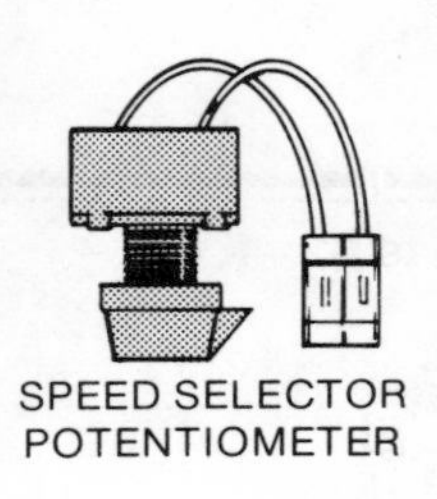

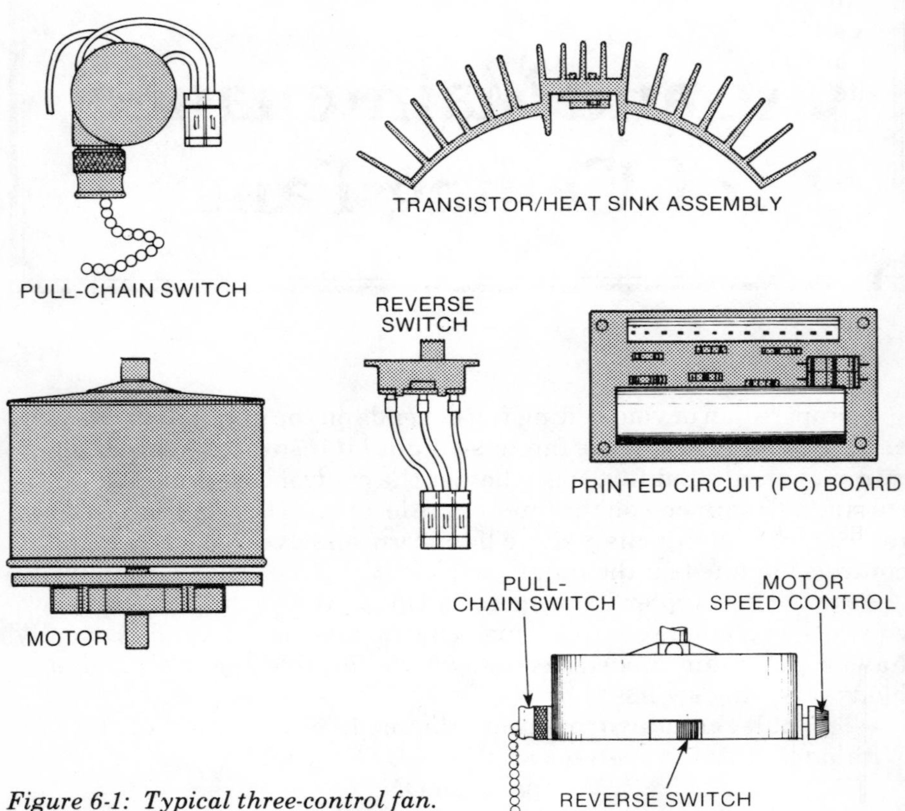

Figure 6-1: Typical three-control fan.

• The reversing switch on the side of the switch housing controls the airflow direction:

left, downward airflow
right, upward airflow.

Generally, a two-control fan (Figure 6-2) has:

• The three-speed pull-chain switch that has four positions:

1. pull, ON—low speed
2. pull again, ON—medium speed
3. pull again, ON—high speed
4. pull again, fan OFF.

• The reversing switch on the side of the switch housing that controls the airflow direction:

left, downward airflow
right, upward airflow.

If lights are installed, a separate pull-chain control is employed to operate the lights (Figure 6-3).

A single-control fan generally only has a pull-chain switch to turn the unit on and to regulate blade speed. There is **no** blade reverse switch. As mentioned earlier, single-control fans are not usually recommended for residential use.

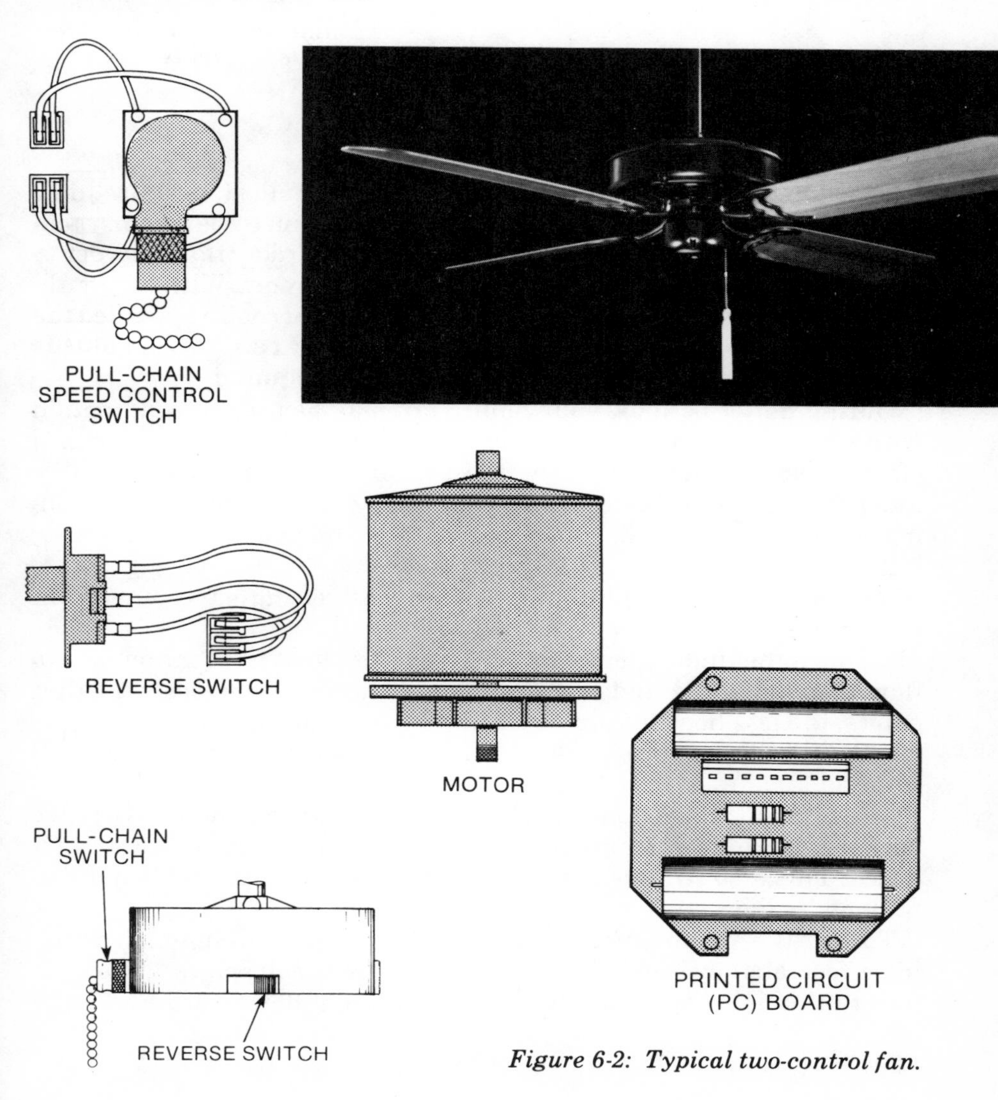

Figure 6-2: Typical two-control fan.

Figure 6-3: With two-control fan models, a separate pull-chain control is required to operate the lights.

FAN OPERATING TIPS

To enjoy the comfort of your ceiling fan to the fullest, here are some helpful tips that you may wish to consider. In warmer weather, as mentioned previously, we recommend use of downward airflow in order to provide a pleasant, gentle swirl of air across the room. With air gently moving across your skin, you feel cool. This kind of cooling is called the windchill factor. For many weeks of the year, it can provide all the cooling you need so that no air conditioning is required.

During hotter periods, your ceiling fan may be used in conjunction with air conditioning to reduce operating cost. Because of the windchill effect, your air conditioning thermostat can usually be raised 6° to 8°, and you will still feel comfortable. For each degree your air conditioning thermostat is raised, you can save 4 to 8% on your air conditioning bill.

Raising your air conditioning thermostat setting saves energy in three ways:

1. The higher indoor temperature allows less heat from the outside to flow through walls and windows to the interior. The less heat that enters, the less heat the air conditioner has to take away.
2. Because there is less heat to take away, your air conditioner will run less.
3. Also, an air conditioner works more efficiently when the difference between the indoor temperature and the outdoor temperature is reduced. This also reduces the stress on your air conditioner, helping to prolong its life.

To keep the air moving sufficiently fast enough to accomplish a cooling effect, airflow is usually set from medium to full speed. The exception to this is in bedroom application where a downward airflow is usually set at low speeds. This gentle breeze is all that is required to keep you comfortable all night long.

In cold weather, we recommend using your ceiling fan with an upward airflow. In cold weather, heated air rises to the ceiling while cool air sinks to the floor. Often there can be a temperature difference between the ceiling and the floor of 15° or more. By circulating air upward from the fan, this warm air is gently pushed off the ceiling, down the side walls of the room, and across the floor. The exact blade speed of your fan depends on the size of the room, number of fans, ceiling height, etc. It should be fast enough to break up the air stratification, but slow enough not to create a draft.

Safe Use of Ceiling Fans

Here are several operational safety tips that you should keep in mind:

- When cleaning, painting, or working near the fan, be careful of the fan and blades. Always turn off the power to the ceiling fan before servicing it or working within the fan blade range. We suggest removal of blades when it is necessary to work near the fan.
- Don't insert anything into the fan blades while the fan is in operation.
- Keep hands, clothing, and other objects away from moving fan blades.
- Exercise close supervision of children when they are around a ceiling fan in operation.
- Never operate a fan that has been damaged in any manner. Contact the manufacturer or the manufacturer's local authorized dealer for assistance in obtaining service.

MAINTENANCE OF CEILING FANS

Most well-designed ceiling fans are virtually carefree. The bearings are sealed, so they require absolutely no servicing, lubrication, or maintenance of any kind. Periodic surface cleaning is the only maintenance needed.

The housing finish may be sealed with lacquer to prevent discoloration or tarnishing; therefore, a soft brush or lint-free cloth should be used to avoid scratching the finish. (If the surface is not sealed with lacquer, the metal housing may require an occasional polishing with a good metal polish.) Surface smudges or accumulations of dirt and dust can easily be removed by using a mild detergent and a soft cloth slightly dampened. An antistatic agent can be used, but never use abrasive cleaning agents which can damage the finish. Occasionally, a light coat of furniture polish may be applied to the wood blades for added protection (Figure 6-4). Polish will also enhance their beauty.

Never saturate a cloth with water to clean your ceiling fan. Excess water introduces the possibility of electrical shock and could lead to blade warpage. Always be certain the fan control switch is in the OFF position before attempting to clean the fan.

Figure 6-4: Protect wooden blades with a light coat of wax.

TROUBLESHOOTING CEILING FANS

While well-designed ceiling fans will give long and reliable operating service, the following general guide (Table 6-1) may help you solve a problem if one should arise. If not, check with the manufacturer's authorized service center.

There are some ceiling fan troubles that require either professional help or a knowledge of electricity. If you have the latter, the following information will be helpful in servicing a ceiling fan. Otherwise, we suggest that you take the fan to your authorized service dealer.

Visual Inspection

Before doing any in-depth troubleshooting, it's wise to give the ceiling fan a good visual inspection. To do this thoroughly:

1. Inspect the fan housing for straightness. Spin the fan blades by hand to be sure that they rotate freely and are not hitting any fan surfaces. If the blade flywheel is striking the switch housing, lift up on the flywheel assembly and tighten the setscrew.
2. Remove the switch housing bottom cap and check all the wire connections at the printed circuit board. Unplug each connector or set of connectors one at a time. Inspect the wire-lead side of each connector; each wire should be fully inserted (Figure 6-5).
3. Inspect for shorted wires to the switch housing (Figure 6-6). Variable speed potentiometer leads and reverse switch leads must have adequate clearance to the switch housing.

Table 6-1: Troubleshooting Guide

Trouble	Possible Cause	Possible Remedies
1) Fan will not start.	1a) No electricity.	1a) Check main and branch circuit fuses or circuit breakers.
	1b) Loose power line connections to fan and switch wire connections in switch housing and/or in canopy.	1b) **Make sure the main power is turned off at the fuse box or circuit breaker,** and check all wire connections. Repair as needed.
	1c) Blade flywheel binding against switch housing.	1c) Adjust and tighten setscrew holding blade flywheel in its proper position.
	1d) Faulty motor.	1d) Replace motor.
2) Fan is noisy during operation.	2a) Light kit glassware is loose or the light bulb is loose in the socket.	2a) Check and tighten screws and/or the light bulb as necessary.
	2b) Loose canopy.	2b) Tighten canopy screws or crossbar assembly.
	2c) The screws securing the fan blade holders to the flywheel are loose.	2c) Tighten the screws.
	2d) Loose blade screws.	2d) Check and tighten as necessary.
	2e) Loose screws in the motor housing.	2e) Make sure all screws in the motor housing are snug but not overly tight.
	2f) Motor pulsating caused by a shorted diode.	2f) Replace electronic printed circuit board.*
	2g) Motor noise caused by solid state wall speed control.	2g) If objectionable, use only variable speed control built in the fan.

*If fan is equipped with a typical electronic speed control.

Table 6-1: Troubleshooting Guide (continued)

Trouble	Possible Cause	Possible Remedies
	2h) Wire nuts inside the switch housing and/or canopy are rattling.	2h) Check and tighten or adjust. **Caution:** Make sure main power is turned OFF.
	2i) Interference between blade flywheel and switch housing.	2i) Check and adjust the blade flywheel setscrew.
	2j) Switch housing has excessive side play.	2j) With some fan models, if the switch housing has excessive side play or fan makes clicking or knocking sound, contact the factory for replacement of side-thrust bushing and instructions.
3) Fan wobbles or shakes excessively. (**Note**: All fans have some wobble.)	3a) Canopy pin not properly fitted in slot on the ball.	3a) Be sure canopy pin is properly set into the slot on the ball.
	3b) The fan blade or its blade holder is not fastened securely.	3b) Check the screws holding the fan blades to the blade holders and the screws holding the blade holders to the blade flywheel. Tighten as necessary.
	3c) The blades are unbalanced.	3c) Switch two adjacent blades, or replace the blades with a balanced set if necessary.
	3d) Fan blade holders are not seated properly.	3d) Check and adjust so that the fan blade holders seat firmly and cleanly to the top surface of the blade flywheel.
	3e) Fan blades are out of alignment.	3e) Check the blade tracking. Adjust the blade height if necessary by bending the blade holder slightly to align the blade height.
	3f) Switch housing has excessive side play.	3f) With some fan models, if the switch housing has excessive side play, contact the factory for replacement of side-thrust bushing.

Symptom Indications

Symptom indications will vary from fan model to fan model. However, certain techniques remain the same.

The following symptom indication guide is intended to assist in solving typical electronic three-control ceiling fan problems with a variable speed potentiometer (Figure 6-7). Some of the trouble symptoms can be readily diagnosed as there are generally only one or two causes which can relate to a particular trouble symptom. In such cases this guide will indicate which component failure relates to the trouble symptom.

Figure 6-5: Inspecting a wire connector.

Figure 6-6: Inspecting for shorted wires.

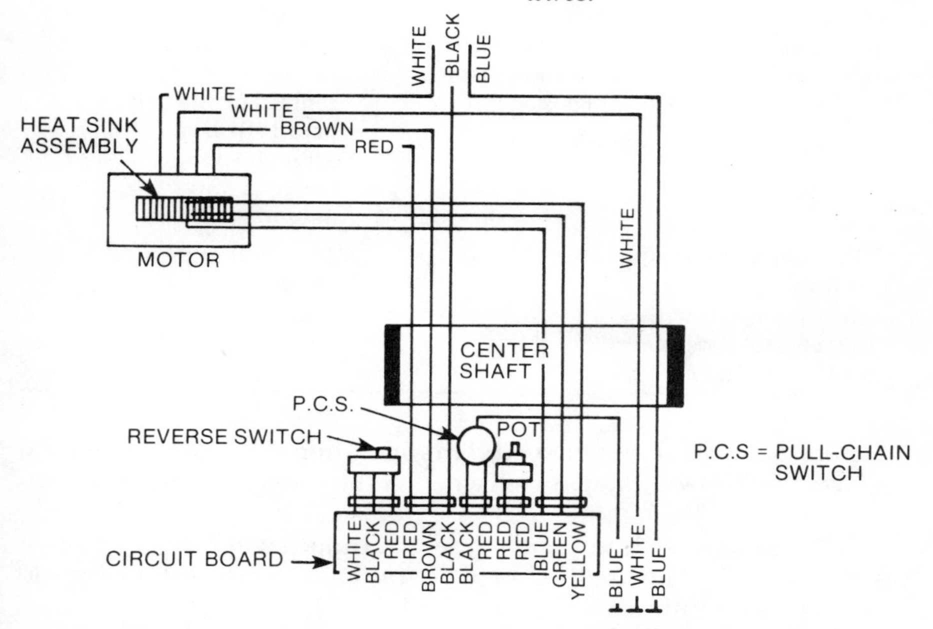

Figure 6-7: Typical electronic three-control ceiling fan block diagram.

Note: The following indication guide (Table 6-2) is for a typical electronically controlled fan; when troubleshooting your fan, use the circuit diagram and data supplied in the manufacturer's service guide.

Table 6-2: Symptom Indication Guide for Three-Control Ceiling Fan

Trouble	Possible Cause	Possible Remedies
1) Fan runs slowly in either direction if rotation is started by hand; will not reverse.	1a) Faulty reverse switch.	1a) Replace reverse switch assembly.
	1b) Faulty capacitor.	1b) Replace printed circuit board (PCB) assembly.
	1c) Open motor winding.	1c) Replace motor assembly.
2) Speed control will not reduce to low speed. Fan operates only at medium and high speed.	2a) Diode shorted.	2a) Replace printed circuit board (PCB) assembly.
	2b) Transistor shorted.	2b) Replace heat sink assembly.
3) Fan motor will not operate at low speed setting. Operation normal at high speed setting.	3a) Open speed control potentiometer.	3a) Replace speed control potentiometer assembly.
	3b) Open or faulty 39-ohm resistor on printed circuit board (PCB) assembly.	3b) If resistor is burned or scorched, replace printed circuit board (PCB) assembly after checking transistor/heat sink assembly.
4) Fan will not operate at full speed. Operates at medium speed with speed control potentiometer set to full speed.	4a) Open diode.	4a) Replace printed circuit board (PCB) assembly.

Before using an ohmmeter to test the operation of the subassemblies, perform the following steps to tell whether the meter is in proper operating condition:

1. With the test leads unplugged, set the range switch on the desired resistance scale. The needle should be stationary at the infinity mark. The symbol for infinity is the "lazy eight" (∞).
2. Plug in the test leads. The meter has two color-coded leads, one red

and the other black. The red lead is used in the positive (+) jack; the black lead is used in the negative (–), or common, jack.

3. Touch the tips of the leads together. The needle should move to the zero position to indicate zero resistance (Figure 6-8).

One of the best methods of testing subassemblies is the ground isolation test. If any subassembly is shorted to ground, the fan can't and won't operate properly. To establish a ground point, set the meter on the **low** ohms scale. Place one lead in the screw hole of the switch housing and the other lead at various places on the switch housing, fan housing, and motor case. In all cases, a zero ohm reading should occur. The isolation tests are conducted between the reference point, i.e., the switch housing screw hole, and each of the connector terminals and printed circuit board terminals.

For the ground test, the resistance range used should be at least 1,000 ohms. This range will read your body resistance; therefore, when making any readings, **don't touch the metal portion of the probes**.

Conduct **all** of the following tests involving insulation displacement connectors with the ohmmeter set as stated in each step. Insert the meter probes into the socket end of the connector.

Mode-Selector Switch. To check the operation of a typical mode-selector pull-chain switch, set the meter on the lowest ohm. Then probe the switch leads and cycle the pull-chain switch (Figure 6-9). The ohmmeter should alternate between open (infinity) and less than 1.0 ohm of resistance.

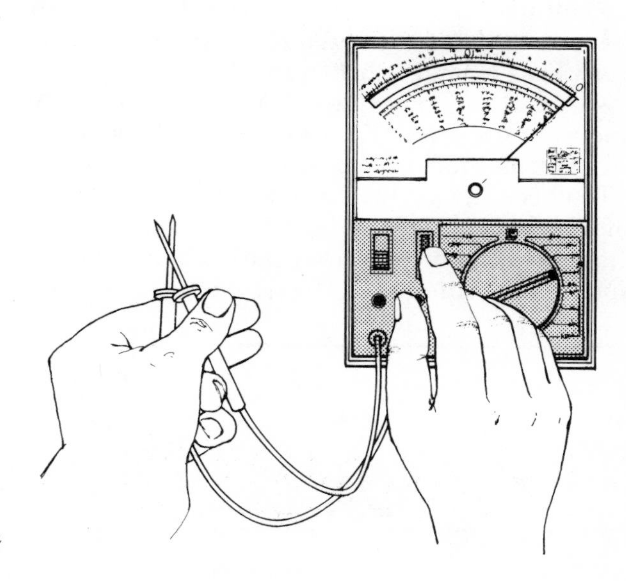

Figure 6-8: Setting an ohmmeter.

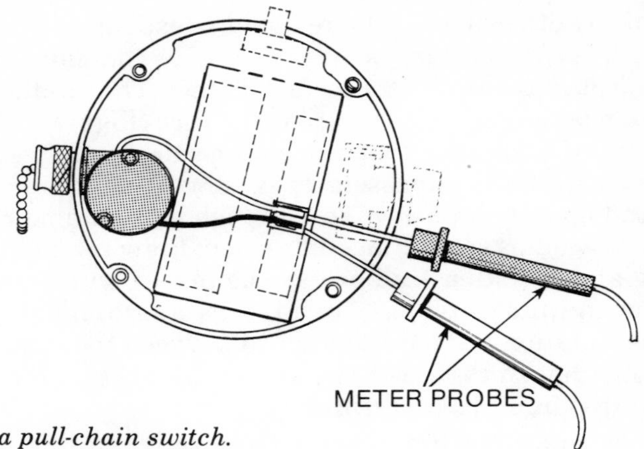

Figure 6-9: Probing a pull-chain switch.

To check the light(s) operation, probe the blue and black lead and cycle the pull-chain switch again. The ohmmeter should read OFF/ON, then ON/OFF. OFF is no reading (infinity); ON is less than 1.0 ohm.

If these results are **not** obtained from the ohmmeter test, **replace the mode-selector pull-chain switch** as directed in the manufacturer's service manual.

Variable Speed Control. Potentiometers—with most good fans—are used to regulate the speed or revolutions per minute (rpm) of the fan blades from very slow to fast. The control achieves this by acting upon the voltage across the fan motor. By reducing the voltage to the motor, the fan motor operates at a reduced power output and, consequently, a lower speed. That is, when the dial is in the extreme counterclockwise position, the fan operates at its slowest speed. As the dial is moved in a clockwise direction (Figure 6-10), the fan speed increases until, when in the extreme clockwise position, it is operating at its fastest speed.

To check the potentiometer, set the ohmmeter on a high ohms scale and probe each of the leads from the potentiometer. The ohmmeter should read from high resistance (about 5,000 ohms) to 0 ohms. The full clockwise position is the 0 (zero) ohms reading.

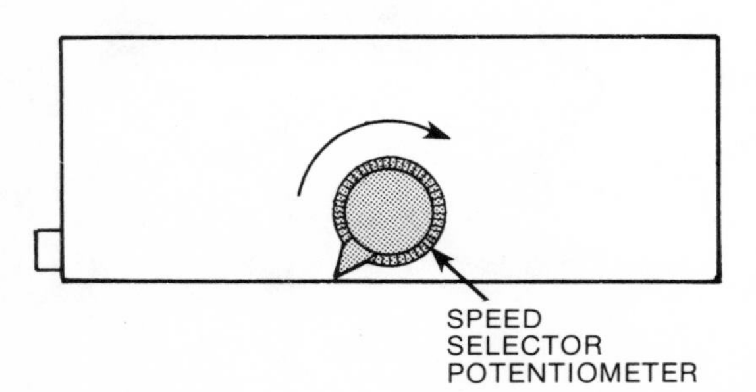

Figure 6-10: Varying the variable speed control.

If these results are **not** obtained from the ohmmeter test, **replace the variable speed potentiometer** as directed in the manufacturer's service manual.

Reverse Switch. The reverse switch (usually a single-pole, double-throw type) controls the airflow patterns of the fan (Figure 6-11). To check the operation of the reverse switch, set the ohmmeter on a low scale, and probe one end lead and center terminal. With the switch in one position, the meter reading should be zero ohms and in the other position, an infinite condition. With the probes on the center and other end terminal, the indications of the meter should be reversed as the switch is moved (Figure 6-12). If these results are **not** obtained from the ohmmeter test, replace the reverse switch.

Transistor/Heat Sink Assembly. More sophisticated ceiling fans use a transistor—operating in conjunction with the potentiometer—to act as a power resistor in series with the fan motor (Figure 6-13). It varies the power to the motor, therefore reducing or increasing the speed of the fan. The excess heat caused by the action of the transistor is dissipated by the heat sink. When checking or replacing a transistor/heat sink assembly, be sure to follow the manufacturer's instructions to the letter.

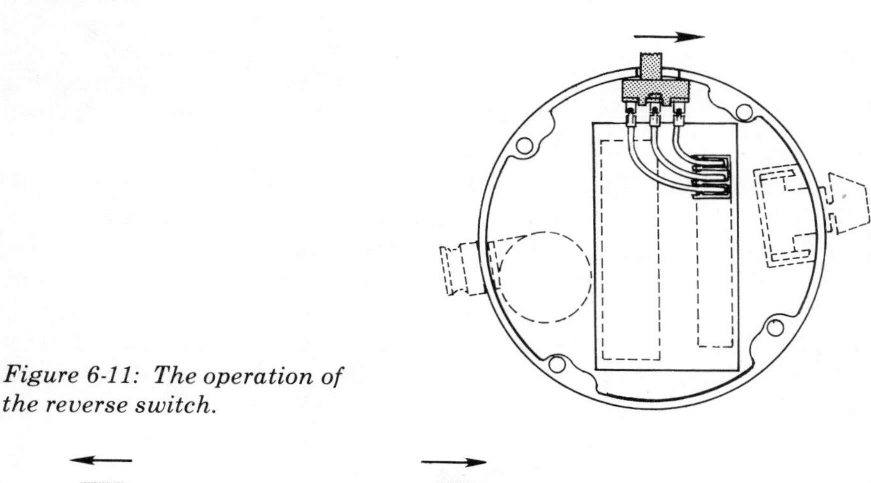

Figure 6-11: The operation of the reverse switch.

RED
WHITE
BLACK
RED
BLACK
WHITE

Figure 6-12: Positioning of the reverse switch.

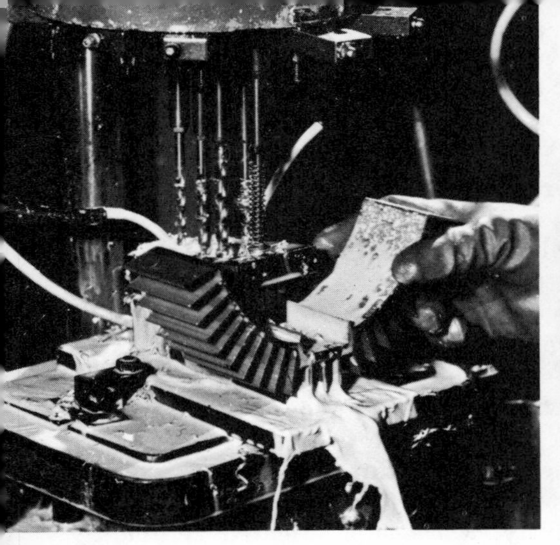

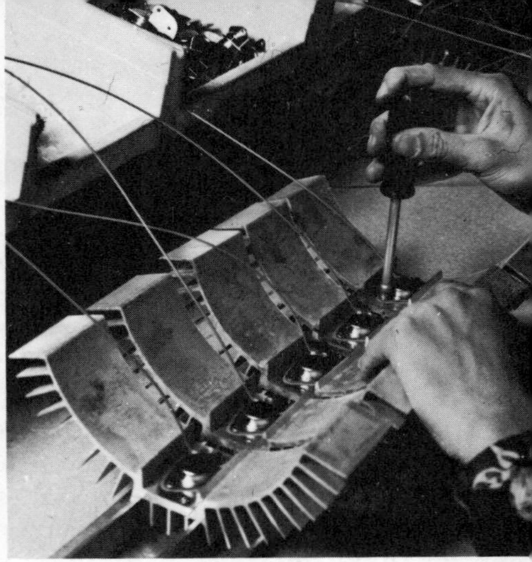

Figure 6-13: The making of heat sinks.

Printed Circuit Board. With many modern electronically controlled ceiling fans, a printed circuit board (PCB) functions as the "heart" of the unit (Figure 6-14). It's the terminus point of all controls—i.e., reverse, mode selector, speed control—as well as the connection point of the motor and heat sink. If your fan has a printed circuit board, test and replace it (if necessary) as instructed in the manufacturer's service manual. As a rule, the printed circuit board must be replaced as a unit, not as separate components.

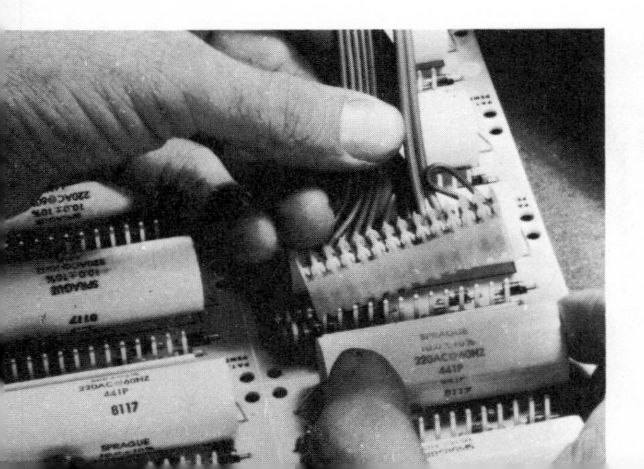

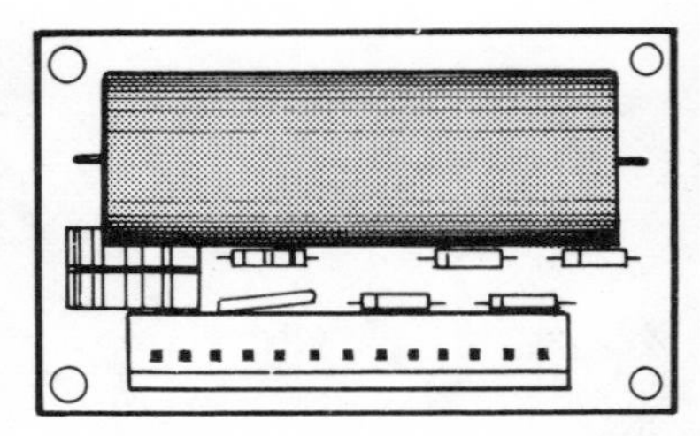

Figure 6-14: Typical printed circuit board.

Figure 6-15 gives the circuit block diagram for a typical two-control ceiling fan unit. Table 6-3, another symptom indication guide, is typical for this type of unit.

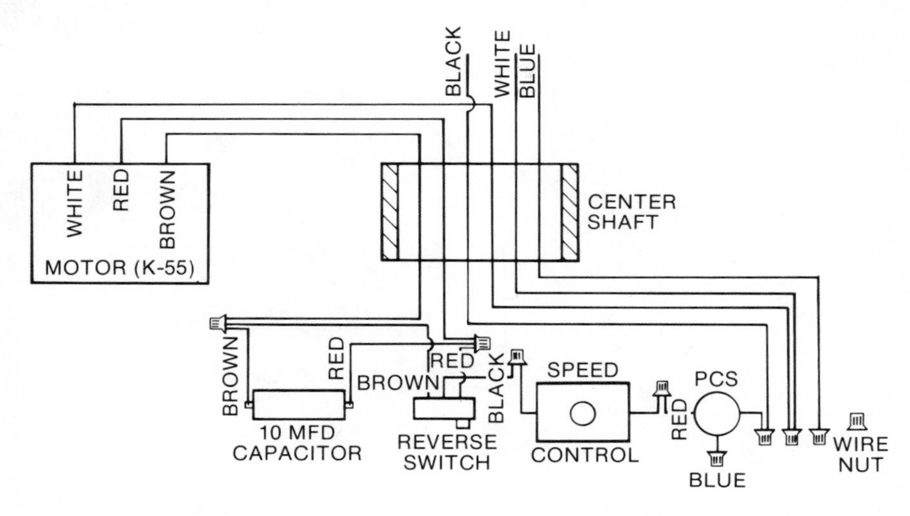

Figure 6-15: Typical circuit block diagram for a two-control ceiling fan unit.

Table 6-3: Symptom Indication Guide for Two-Control Ceiling Fan

Trouble	Possible Cause	Possible Remedies
1) Fan runs slowly in either direction if rotation is started by hand; will not reverse.	1a) Faulty reverse switch. 1b) Faulty capacitor. 1c) Motor has open winding.	1a) Replace reverse switch assembly. 1b) Replace printed circuit board (PCB) assembly. 1c) Replace motor assembly.
2) Fan will not operate at proper speeds or will not operate at any speed.	2a) Faulty three-speed pull-chain control. 2b) Faulty capacitor.	2a) Replace three-speed pull-chain control assembly. 2b) Replace printed circuit board (PCB) assembly.

A shorted or open capacitor can be tested with an ohmmeter (Figure 6-16). When a capacitor is open, the needle won't deflect from the infinity or AT-REST position. When shorted, the needle will deflect and remain at or near the zero resistance point. Capacitance is indicated when the needle deflects toward zero, then returns to the infinity position.

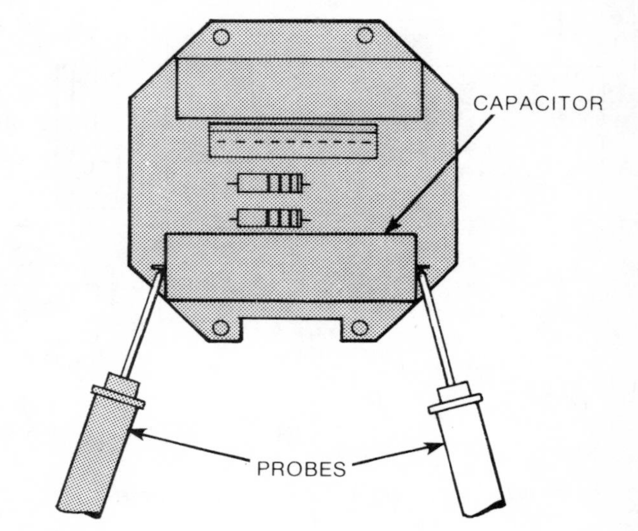

Figure 6-16: Checking a capacitor.

Voltage Checks

Some trouble symptoms such as an inoperative fan motor are more difficult to troubleshoot. In these cases it is necessary to use a systematic approach to isolate the cause of failure. Accordingly, the following guide provides a list of check points where voltage can be conveniently measured. Absence of AC voltage at a check point will isolate the failure to one of several causes which should be checked in the order indicated.

To set up for the test procedure, a suitable voltmeter capable of reading approximately 200 volts AC is needed. Connect the common probe to the white neutral wire labeled LIGHTS in the switch housing. The remaining probe is then used to contact the selected check points (Figure 6-17).

Table 6-4 shows how to proceed with typical voltage checks for the fan unit shown in Figure 6-7. Check the manufacturer's service manual for exact instructions for conducting voltage checks on your fan.

Figure 6-17: Making a voltage check.

Table 6-4: Voltage Checks for Three-Control Ceiling Fan

Check Point	Possible Cause	Corrective Action
Black power wire on motor connector.		
if — No Voltage	1) Tripped circuit breaker or blown fuse.	1) Reset circuit breaker or replace fuse.
ok	2) Faulty house wiring.	2) Have electrician check.
	3) Faulty connection in ceiling box or canopy wiring.	3) Check and correct fault.
↓ Black lead on pull-chain switch connector.		
if — No Voltage	1) Wire not properly connected in wire nut.	1) Reconnect.
ok ↓		
Red lead in pull-chain switch connector.		
if — No Voltage	1) Defective pull-chain switch.	1) Replace switch.
ok ↓	2) Wire not properly connected in wire nut.	2) Reconnect.

Table 6-4: Voltage Checks for Three-Control Ceiling Fan (continued)

Check Point	Possible Cause	Corrective Action
Black lead on reverse switch connector.		
(if) → No Voltage	1) Open lead. 2) Improper wire connection in wire nut.	1) Repair. 2) Reconnect.
ok ↓		
Red wire on reverse switch.		
(if) → No Voltage	1) Improper wire connection in wire nut. 2) Defective reverse switch. 3) Open capacitor.	1) Reconnect. 2) Replace reverse switch. 3) Replace defective capacitor.
ok ↓		
White wire on reverse switch.		
(if) → No Voltage	1) Improper wire connection in wire nut. 2) Defective reverse switch. 3) Open capacitor.	1) Remate connector. 2) Replace reverse switch. 3) Replace defective capacitor.
ok ↓		
Red wire on motor connector or brown wire on motor connector.		
(if) → No Voltage	1) Improper wire connection in wire nut. 2) Open motor winding.	1) Reconnect. 2) Remove wire from connector. Strip 1/4″ of insulation from end and check resistance with ohm-voltmeter. Should read 60 ± 10 ohms. If no resistance reading is obtained, winding is open and motor must be replaced. **Remember, power must be OFF when checking with ohmmeter.**

FAN WOBBLE

Occasionally, your ceiling fan may exhibit wobble during operation. This is probably due to some kind of irregularity in blades and/or the blade irons. We suggest the following procedure be followed to remedy such a situation:

1. Check that all blades are screwed firmly into the blade holder.
2. Check that all blade holders are tightly secured.
3. Looking up at the fan from below, make sure that none of the blade irons are bent so that a blade is out of position. Correction may be made by gently bending the blade iron back into position.
4. Blade tracking may be checked simply by use of a household yardstick as shown in Figure 6-18. Place the yardstick vertically against the ceiling and even with the outside leading edge of a blade. Note the distance from the edge of the blade to the ceiling. Turn the blades slowly by hand to check the remaining blades. If a blade isn't in alignment, the blade iron may be gently bent up or down to be in line with the other blades.

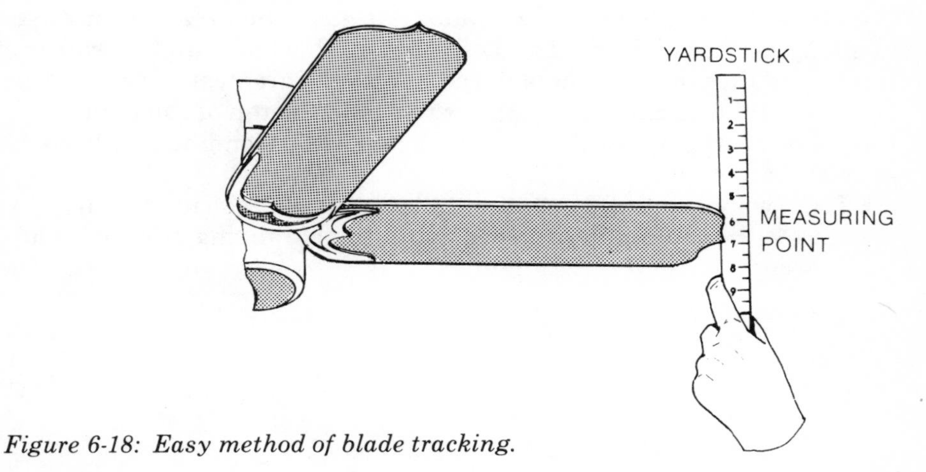

Figure 6-18: Easy method of blade tracking.

5. If these steps don't solve the wobble problem, a dynamic balancing should be done using the blade balancing kit. The following procedure is typical of one of the more popular balancing kits. (Check the manufacturer of your fan for the best type of kit or balancing technique recommended.)

• Turn the fan on and adjust the speed control knob setting to a speed at which wobble is the greatest.

• Stop the fan. Select one blade and place the balancing clip on it, midway between the blade holder and the blade tip (Figure 6-19).

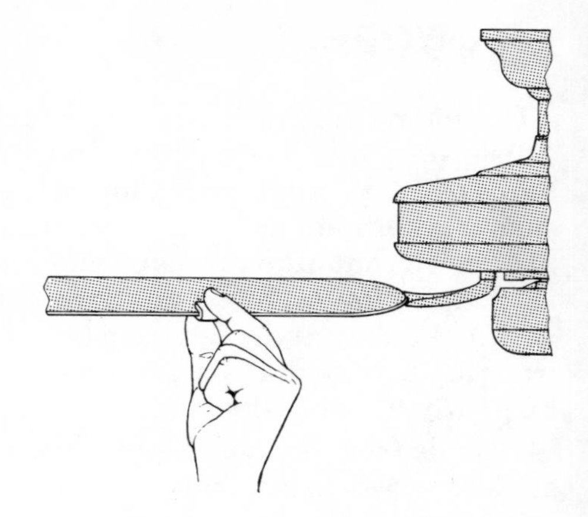

Figure 6-19: Applying balancing clip to a blade.

• Start the fan. Note whether the wobble is worsened or improved. Stop the fan again, move the clip to another blade, and retest. Repeat this process on all blades, noting the blade on which the greatest improvement is achieved.

• Move the clip back to the blade that gave the greatest improvement. Move the clip inward and outward on this blade and operate the fan to find the position where the clip gives the greatest improvement.

• Install the balancing weight provided to the top of the blade near the point where the clip is installed (Figure 6-20). Generally, only a single weight is required.

• If the wobble problem is not completely solved, you may wish to try to improve the balancing further using the balancing clip and additional weights.

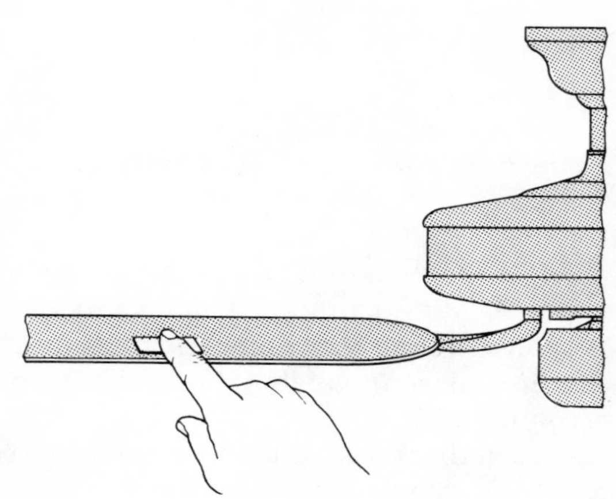

Figure 6-20: Adding balancing weight to a blade.

CHAPTER 7

Special Installation Considerations

When installing a ceiling fan, there are several special considerations that should be kept in mind. In addition to how the ceiling fan should be installed (this is covered in detail in Chapter 5), there are such options as lighting kits, wall controls, and various wiring arrangements to consider. These options can make the operation of your fan more versatile and convenient.

LIGHT KITS

Light kits are available for your ceiling fan that will not only provide light, if needed, but will also complement the beauty of the fan and the decor of your room (Figure 7-1).

Figure 7-1: Light kits add beauty to ceiling fans.

Most fan manufacturers offer a full line of matching light kits and glassware (Figure 7-2). These lighting kits are generally available in single-, four-, and five-light designs.

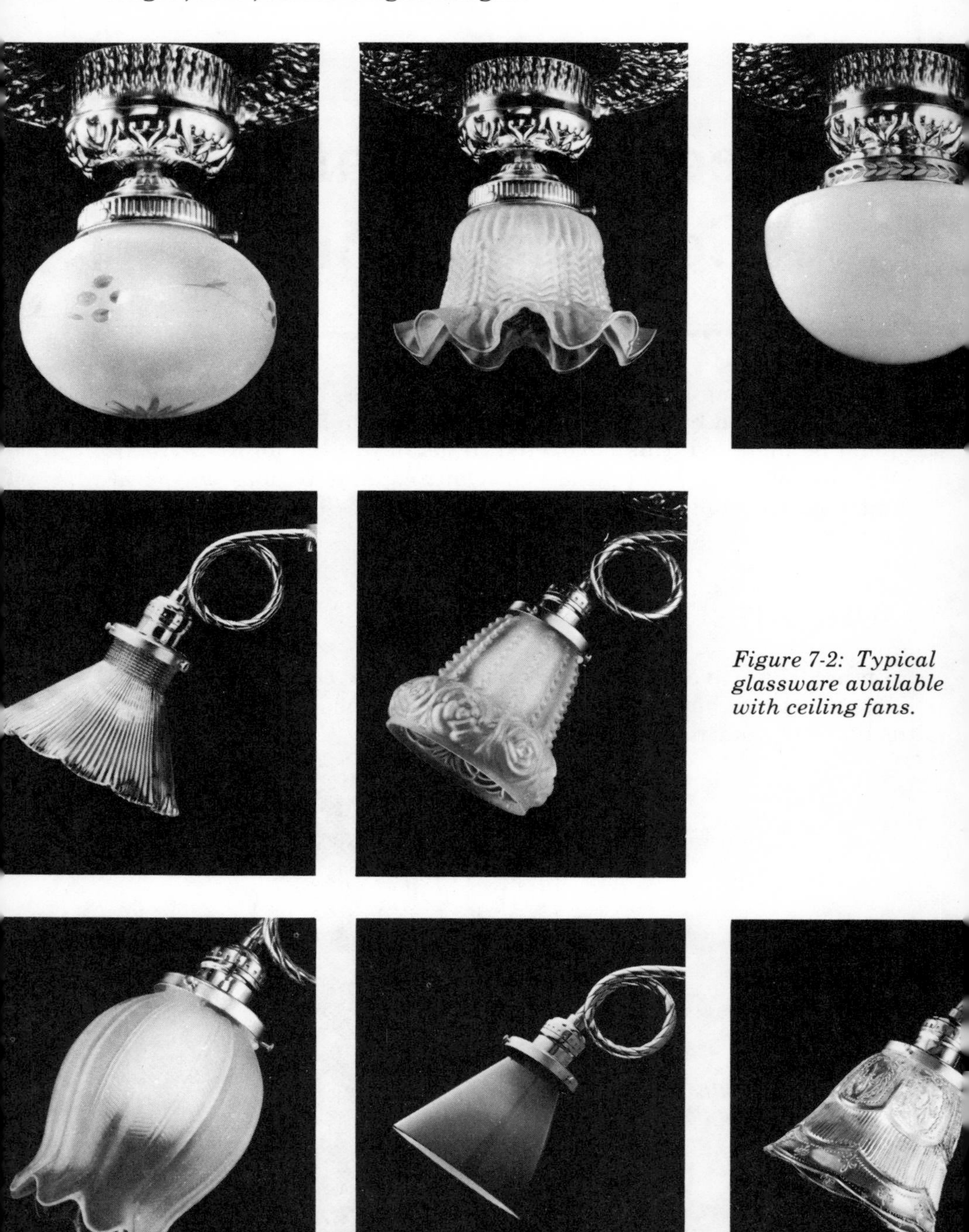

Figure 7-2: Typical glassware available with ceiling fans.

• Single-light kits (Figure 7-3A) usually permit up to 100 watts of illumination.

• Four-light kits (Figure 7-3B) give a more formal look. Four 60-watt bulbs may generally be used for up to 240 watts of illumination.

• Five-light kits (Figure 7-3C) add a center light and usually permit up to 300 watts of illumination.

Note: Be sure to use **only** a light kit recommended by the manufacturer of the fan. When the failure of a fan is caused by the use of a light kit **not** recommended by the fan manufacturer, the manufacturer usually voids the warranty.

A

B

Figure 7-3: Three major styles of fan light kits.

C

Installing a Light Kit

To obtain proper results from a light kit, it must be installed and operated as directed in the owner's manual. For ease of installation it's advisable, if possible, to install the light kit **before** hanging the ceiling fan. Also, before assembling and installing the light kit, **read** the manufacturer's instructions **thoroughly** for the type and model of light kit that you have purchased. Remove all the parts from the shipping carton and check them against the list of parts found in the package. **Caution: When installing any light kit, be sure to disconnect the electric circuit supplying power to the fan prior to installing the unit.** This will avoid the possibility of serious injury due to electrical shock. Also, when removing and tightening screws, make certain not to scratch the metal surfaces with the screwdriver.

To give you some idea of what is involved, let's look at the instructions for a single-light mount on a three-control fan unit. The installation proceeds as follows:

1. After the power to the fan has been turned OFF, remove the two screws (A) and plug (B) around the switch housing at the bottom of the fan (Figure 7-4).
2. Feed the lamp unit wire through the plug hole in the bottom cap and screw the lamp unit onto the cap. Tighten securely.
3. Connect the two wires from the lamp unit (C) to the two wires in the switch housing marked LIGHTS (Figure 7-5). Connect the white wire to the white wire and the black wire from the lamp to the colored wire in the switch housing. Strip 1/2″ of insulation off the wire ends, leaving the exposed metal. Twist the designated wire ends together; using the wire nuts provided, insert the wire into the nut, also in a twisting motion.

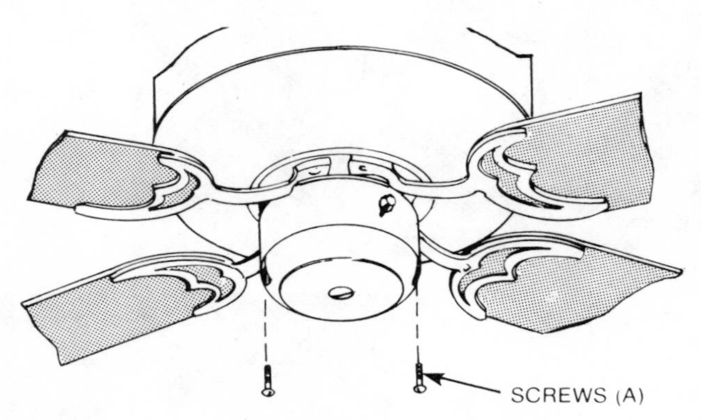

Figure 7-4: Installing a single-light kit mount.

4. Reinstall the bottom cap with the screws from step 2 removed.
5. Install a light bulb, and install the thumb screws (D). Install the glass shade; tighten the thumb screws moderately finger-tight to secure glass shade (E). Do **not** tighten the thumb screws with pliers.
6. Turn power ON and verify operation of the fan and lights. The mode control pull-chain is a four-way switch that operates as follows: OFF; pull, FAN ONLY; pull, LIGHTS ONLY; pull, BOTH FAN AND LIGHTS.

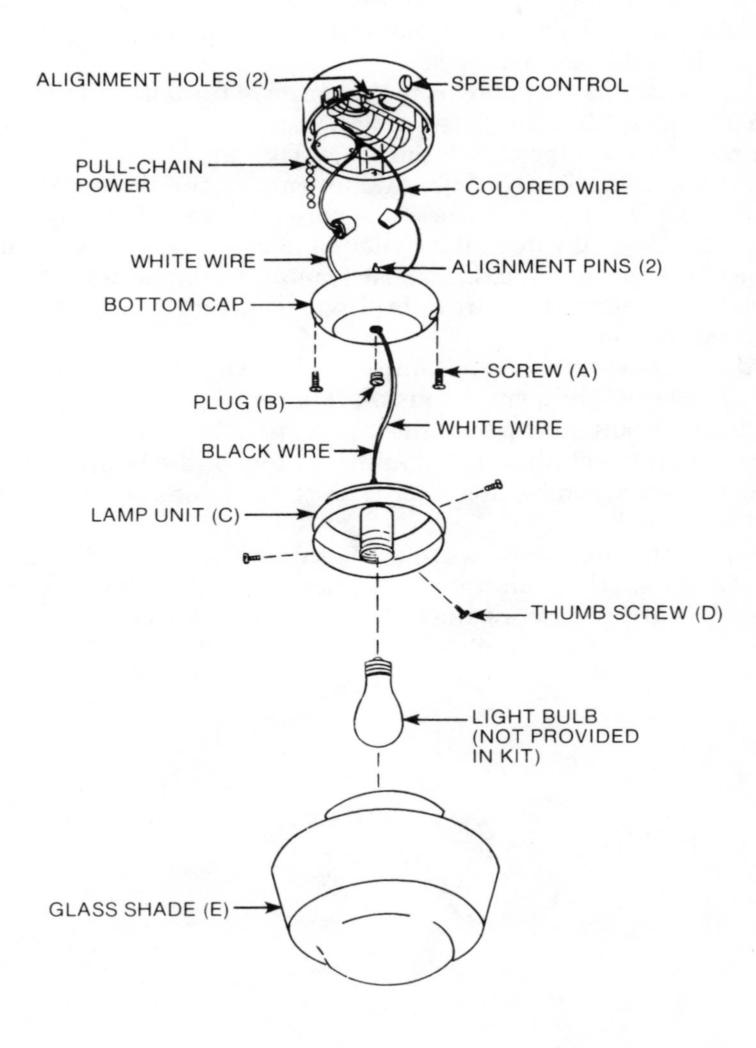

Figure 7-5: Parts of a single-light kit mount.

The installations of four- and five-light kits are similar. The installation of a typical five-light kit to a three-control ceiling fan unit is as follows:

1. After the power to the fan has been turned OFF, remove the two screws (A) around the switch housing at the bottom of the fan (Figure 7-6).
2. With the lamp arms curved downward, connect the two free wires marked LIGHTS from the lamp ring to the two wires located in the switch housing marked LIGHTS (white wire to white wire). Strip 1/2″ of insulation off the wire end, leaving exposed metal. Twist the designated wire ends together.
3. Remove the slotted plug from the center of the bottom cap. Feed the lamp unit wire (C) through the plug hole in the bottom cap and screw the lamp unit onto the cap (Figure 7-7). Tighten securely.
4. Connect the two wires from the lamp unit to the wires joined above. Connect the white wire to the white wire and the black wire from the lamp to the colored wire in the switch housing. Strip 1/2″ of insulation off the wire ends, leaving the exposed metal. Twist the designated wire ends together; using the wire nuts provided, insert the wire into the nut in a twisting motion.
5. Align the two pins on the lamp unit ring with the shallow pin holes on the bottom of the switch housing (Figure 7-7).
6. Place the bottom cap onto the lamp unit. Align the pins on the bottom cap with the shallow holes in the bottom of the lamp unit.
7. Screw the assembly together with the two longer screws (B) provided with the kit.
8. Attach the thumb screws to the lamp socket, followed by the glass shades. Tighten the thumb screws moderately finger-tight to secure the shades (Figure 7-8). Screw the light bulbs in the sockets.

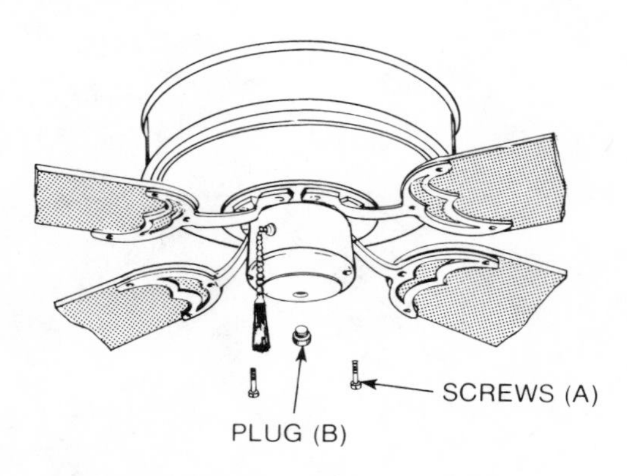

Figure 7-6: Preparing to install a five-light kit mount.

9. Turn power ON and verify operation of the fan and lights. The mode-control pull-chain is a four-way switch that operates as follows: OFF; pull, FAN ONLY; pull, LIGHTS ONLY; pull, BOTH FAN AND LIGHTS.

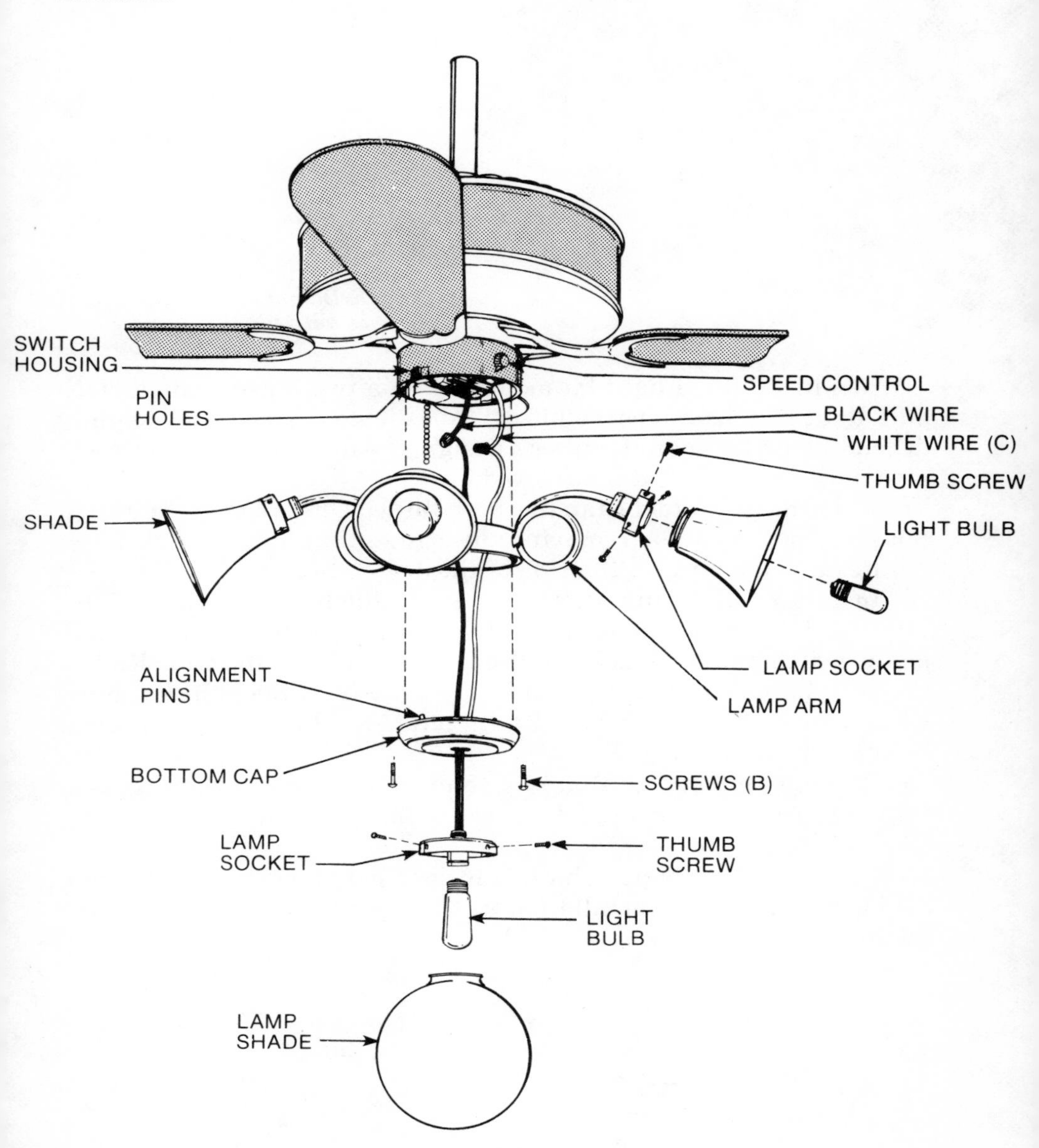

Figure 7-7: Parts of a five-light kit mount.

Figure 7-8: Tightening the thumb screws on the glass shade. Do not tighten the thumb screws with pliers.

When installing a light kit mounting on a two-control fan, an ON-OFF light switch must be installed. While the steps may change slightly depending on the manufacturer's design, the following procedure will give an idea as to what is involved:

1. After the power to the fan has been turned OFF, remove the switch housing bottom cap by removing the screws that hold it in place.
2. Remove the plug on the side of the switch housing.
3. Install a pull-chain switch provided in the light kit (Figure 7-9).
4. Attach the blue wire in the switch housing to one lead on the pull-chain switch and the black wire from the light kit to the other lead on the pull-chain switch. Attach the white wire from the light kit to the white wire in the switch housing (Figure 7-10). Proceed with normal light kit installation.
5. For single circuit installations, connect the blue and black wires at the top of the fan together and connect to the colored wire in the ceiling (Figure 7-10).
6. Once the ON-OFF pull-chain light switch is properly installed, proceed with the light kit installation for the type of mounting that is to be installed.

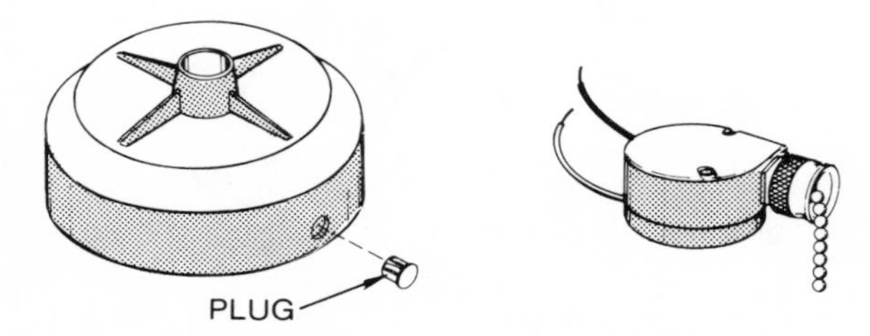

Figure 7-9: Installing a pull-chain switch.

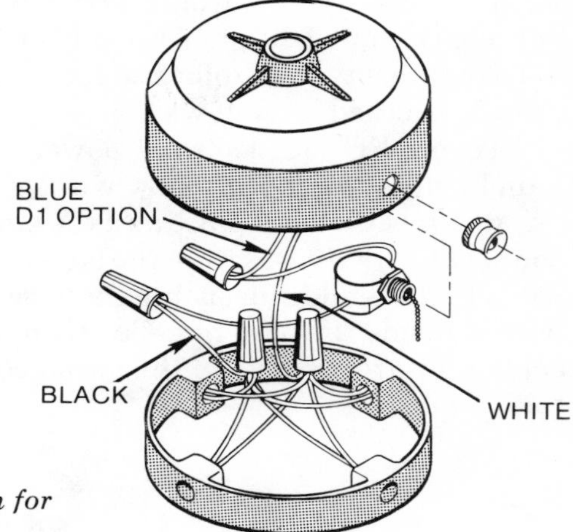

Figure 7-10: Typical circuit diagram for lighting kit on a two-control fan.

WALL CONTROLS

As described in Chapter 3, solid state wall controls provide finger-tip control of the ceiling fan's speed from a convenient wall location. Most wall controls are designed to replace a standard wall switch and will fit a depth of 2″ or greater; that is, when replacing a ceiling light or chandelier, you can utilize the wall switch's wiring (two-wire plus ground) for the wall control. **Note:** All solid state wall controls may cause objectionable fan motor noise. Their use is **not** recommended in applications where extreme quiet is desired, such as bedrooms.

When selecting a solid state wall control, make certain that it has at least a 4-ampere rating. This rating allows for one typical fan and up to 300 watts of lights or up to four fans on a single control (Figure 7-11). Al-

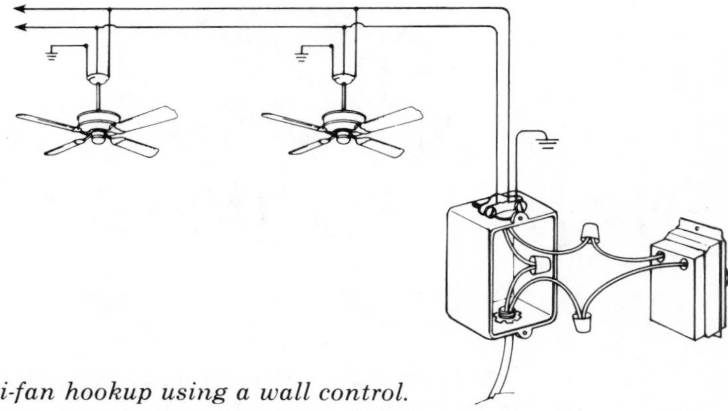

Figure 7-11: Multi-fan hookup using a wall control.

ways connect the control in series with the fan motor(s) and the line voltage (Figure 7-12); never connect the control across line voltage.

To install a typical solid state wall control in place of an existing wall switch, proceed as follows:

1. Turn OFF the electrical power at the fuse box or circuit breaker panel before attempting any wiring.

2. Remove the wall plate and the standard two-wire wall switch. Disconnect the two wires from the old switch and connect the speed control wires to the wall leads, using the wire nuts provided. Make sure all bare wire is inside the wire nut. **Caution:** Don't connect ground wire (bare, copper, or green wire) to the speed control.

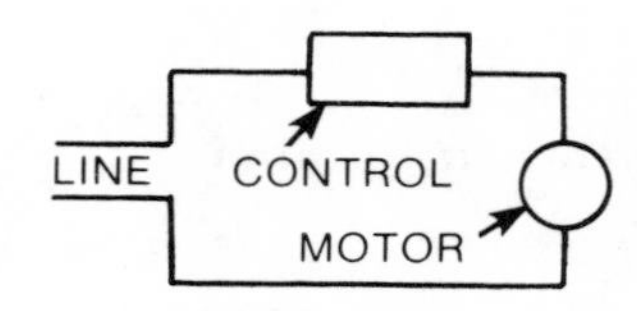

Figure 7-12: Proper hookup for a wall control.

3. Mount the fan speed control in the wall box (Figure 7-13A). Turn the power ON. The fan speed control on the fan should be adjusted to maximum or full speed. A minimum speed adjustment is provided to allow independent control of the minimum speed setting. A small screwdriver is needed for this adjustment.

4. With the fan motor(s) in actual operating condition, turn the main control shaft a full turn in a clockwise direction to the lowest speed position. Locate the adjustment hole near the middle of the front plate (Figure 7-13B). Rotate the adjustment screw clockwise to decrease the minimum speed. A minimum fan speed of approximately 30 rpm has been found to be ideal. Lower speeds may lead to occasional motor stalling and should be **avoided.**

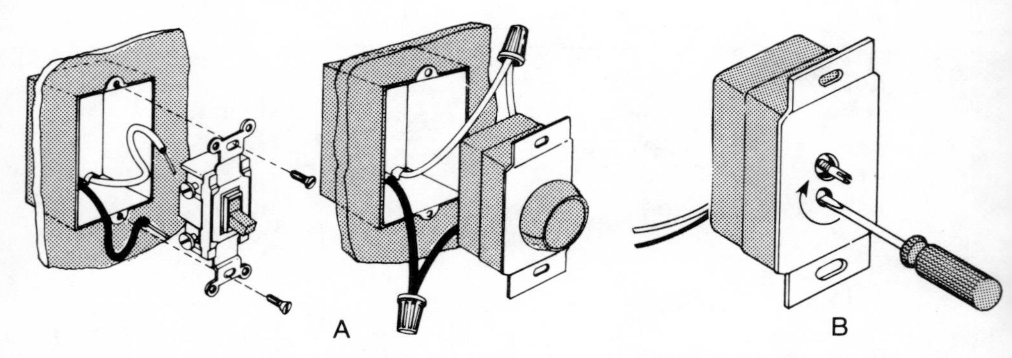

Figure 7-13: (A) Mounting a wall control in an electric wall box. (B) Adjusting the low-speed adjustment.

5. Turn the control shaft counterclockwise until the control switch snaps OFF. Replace the wall plate. With the pointer aligned to the OFF position, push the control knob onto the shaft.

If installing a wall control in an installation where there is no wall outlet available, a cable—either BX or nonmetallic—must be run (generally parallel to the joists) from the fan unit to the wall control and on to a power source, which may be an outlet box, receptacle, or the main power source. Measure the distance across the ceiling from the fan to the wall and down to the control. To this, add the distance to the power source. Then, to this figure, add two additional feet to get the total amount of wire needed.

The electric box for the control should be located 4′ from the floor. The installation of the box will depend on the type of wall construction. With lath and plaster walls, first locate a wall stud; methods of locating studs are given on page 76. Cut an opening in the plaster 5″ out from the stud, large enough to expose the laths. Use the electric box to outline the cut to be made in the wall (Figure 7-14A). Then remove the plaster with a chisel and drill saw holes. Hold your hand against the plaster to prevent cracks. Cut away the lath as necessary (Figure 7-14B).

Punch the knockout disks from the electric box. Pull the wiring from the fan and the electric power source through the proper holes. (The method of running the electric cables through the ceiling and wall is given in Chapter 5.) Attach the connectors and install the locknuts. Push the box into the hole in the wall and anchor the box to the lath with wood screws (Figure 7-14C).

In drywall or wood paneling, boxes can be mounted between studs by means of special clamping devices that grip the inside of the hollow wall (Figure 7-15). The strongest point in this type of wall construction, however, is at the studs. You can get electric boxes equipped with brackets that can be nailed or screwed directly to the face of the studwork. To fit boxes directly onto the studs, you must first locate the stud, then clip a notch out of the drywall large enough to accept the fastening bracket (Figure 7-16A). Connect the wires to the box before placing it in the hole (Figure 7-16B). When the installation is complete, patch the hole with either spackle or plaster so that it is flush with the wall surface (Figure 7-16C).

Once the electric box is installed, the wall control can be installed as previously described when replacing an existing wall switch.

OPTIONAL WIRING METHODS

There are several wiring and operation alternatives available to owners of ceiling fans. Most fans are usually wired in the traditional manner, with all controls on the fans. These conventional built-in

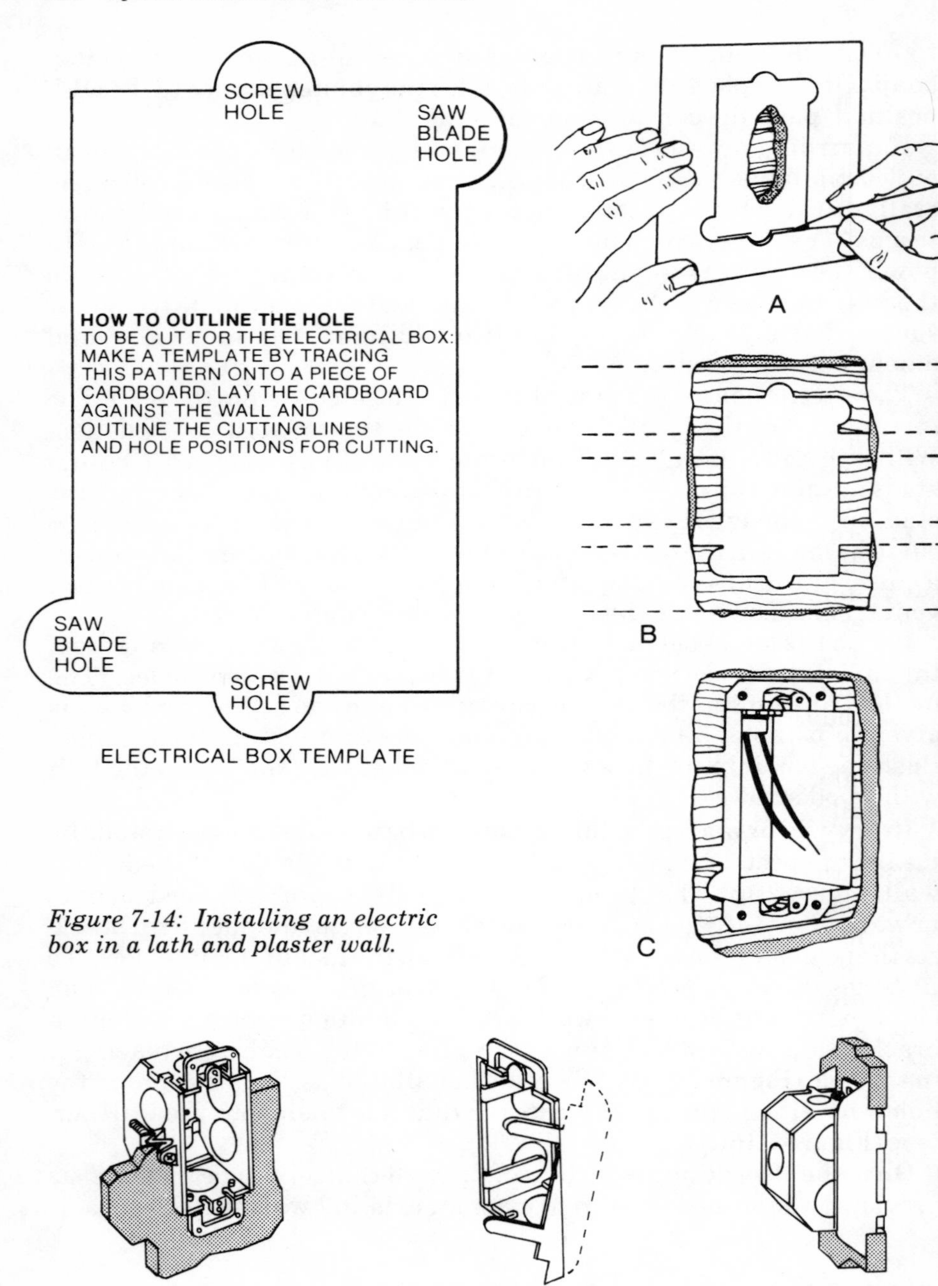

Figure 7-14: Installing an electric box in a lath and plaster wall.

Figure 7-15: Steps in mounting an electric wall box between studs in drywall with box clamps: (Left) Clamps grip rear side of wall as side screws are tightened. (Center) Or use metal supports that slip in the hole. (Right) The projecting tabs are bent into the box.

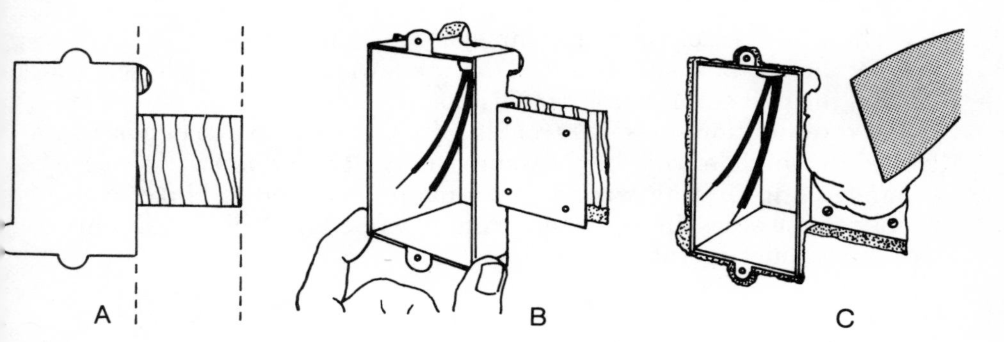

Figure 7-16: Installing an electric box in drywall using a stud for support.

wiring circuits may include a fan only or a fan and a light. Their operations are described on page 112.

Before attempting any optional wiring arrangements, take the cover off of the switch housing and study the wiring as the unit comes from the factory. This will give a better understanding of interpreting manufacturer's wiring diagrams.

The following wiring diagrams are for a typical three-speed control—pull-chain mode switch, variable speed control, and reverse switch—fan. Study these diagrams against the basic wiring diagram of your fan and you will be able to work the proper wiring procedure. These optional wiring methods are:

1. Wall Switch Control of the Fan (Figure 7-17).
   - No light kit is used.
   - Set the pull-chain to the fan ON position.
   - No changes in household or fan wiring are required.

If the fan is replacing a ceiling light or chandelier, you can utilize the wall switch as a control to turn the fan OFF and ON.

2. Wall Control Replaces Wall Switch (Figure 7-18).
   - No light kit is used.
   - No changes in fan wiring are required.

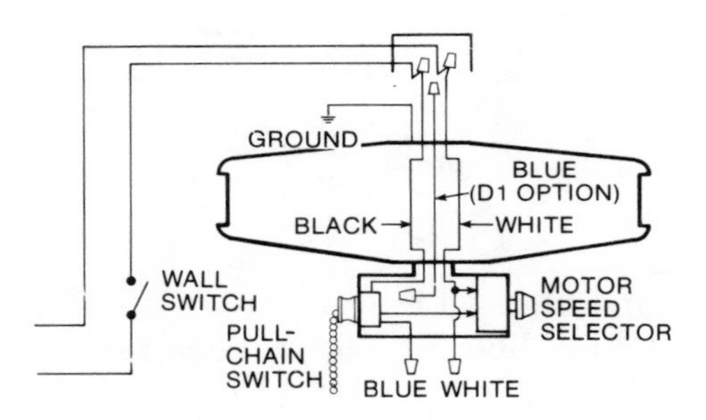

Figure 7-17

- The wall control varies the fan speed.
- Set the variable speed control (on the fan) to maximum speed.
- Set the pull-chain to the fan ON position.

The combination speed-control dial and ON-OFF switch can be controlled in a double-gang box. Be sure the switch and fan are properly grounded and that all wiring conforms to local codes. **Note:** Noise problems are a possibility when using a wall control; don't use where extremely quiet operation is desired.

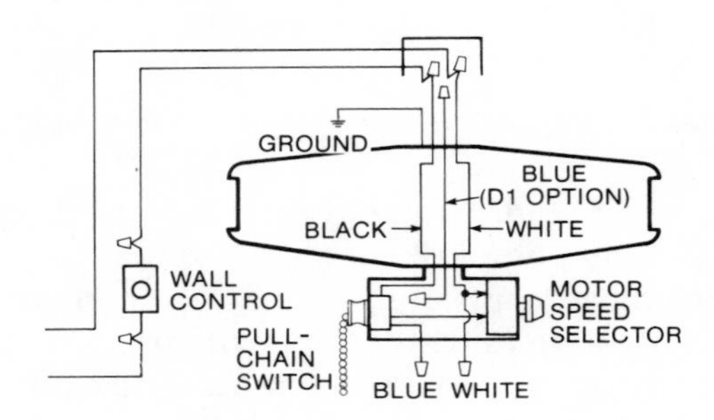

Figure 7-18

3. Wall Switch Control of All Power to Fan and Lights (Figure 7-19).
   - No changes in household wiring are required.
   - The pull-chain switch on the fan governs mode selection:

pull, fan ON
pull again, lights ON
pull again, fan and lights ON
pull again, both OFF.

If the fan is replacing a ceiling light or chandelier, you can utilize the present wall switch to control power to both the fan and the lights.

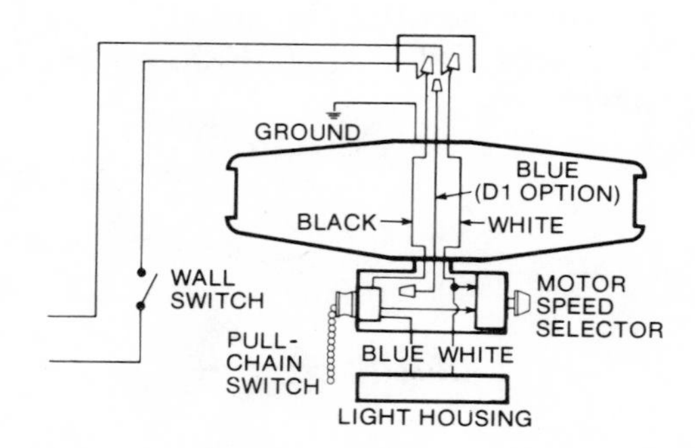

Figure 7-19

4. Wall Control Operates All Power to Fan and Lights (Figure 7-20).
   - No changes in household wiring are required.

• The pull-chain switch on the fan governs mode selection:

pull, fan ON
pull again, lights ON
pull again, fan and lights ON
pull again, both OFF.

• Set variable speed control on the fan to maximum speed.

The wall control regulates all the power to the fan, varies the speed of the fan, and dims the lights. (The faster the fan rotates, the brighter the light will be.)

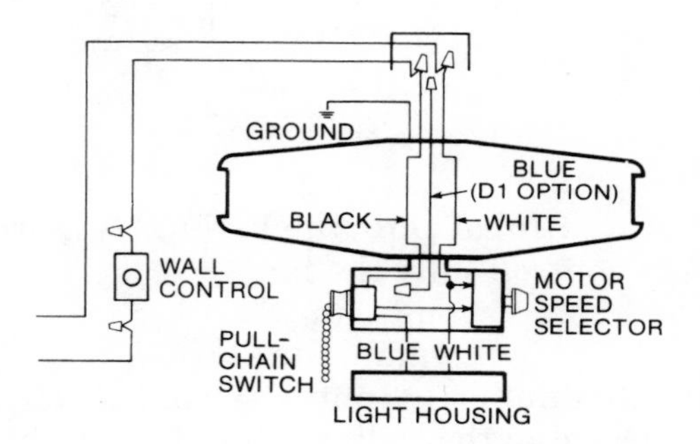

Figure 7-20

5. Operation at Fan (Figure 7-21).
   • With or without light kit.
   • No wall switch.
   • Fan controlled by pull-chain switch:
     Without light kit: Same as 1.
     With light kit: Same as 3.

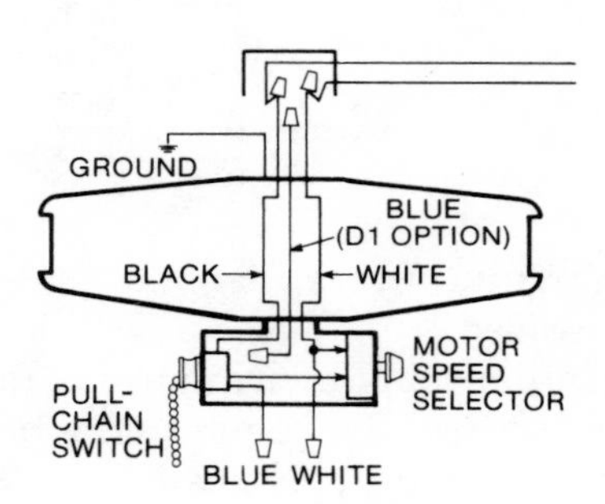

Figure 7-21

6. Wall Switch Control of Only the Light(s) (Figure 7-22).
   • The pull-chain controls only the fan:

pull, fan ON
pull again, fan OFF.

For the wall switch to operate only the light(s), the household hot wire must be connected in the ceiling outlet box as shown.

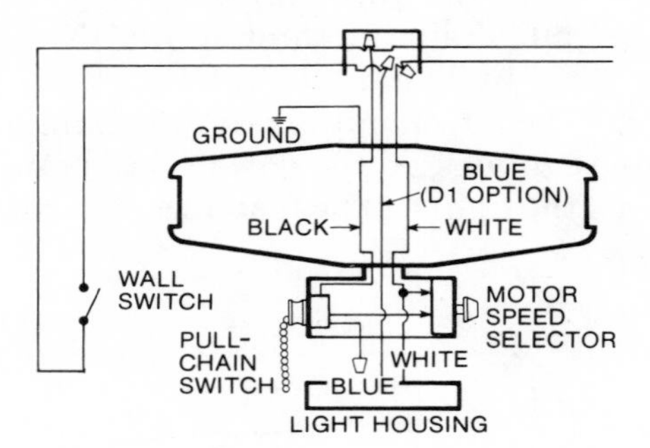

Figure 7-22

7. Light Dimmer Control of Only the Light(s) (Figure 7-23).
   - The pull-chain controls only the fan:

     pull, fan ON

     pull again, fan OFF.

When using a light dimmer to control the light(s), the household hot wire must be connected in the ceiling outlet box as shown.

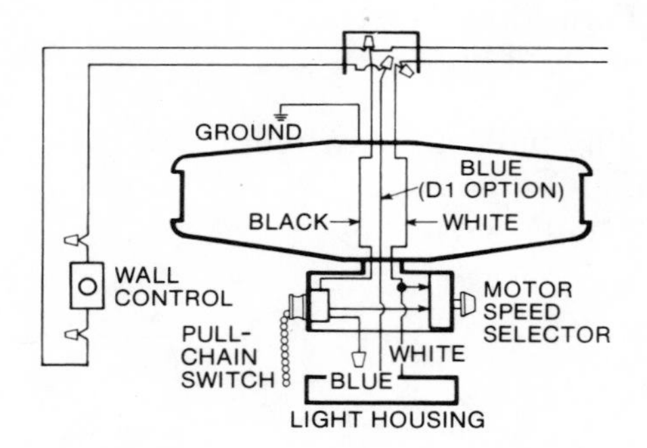

Figure 7-23

8. Three-Way Circuit (Figure 7-24).
   - No light kit is used.
   - No changes in household wiring are required.
   - Wall switches control the power to the fan.
   - Set pull-chain to the fan ON position.

Existing three-way wiring systems may be used to control the power to the fan motor. If a light kit is used, Figure 7-25 shows how it is hooked into a three-way wiring system. In this arrangement the operational mode selection is controlled by the pull-chain on the fan:

1. pull, fan ON

2. pull again, light ON
3. pull again, fan and light ON
4. pull again, both OFF.

All the wiring discussed to this point employs household wiring already in existence. If new wiring is required, it is recommended that this work be performed by a licensed electrician unless you are thoroughly familiar with home wiring systems.

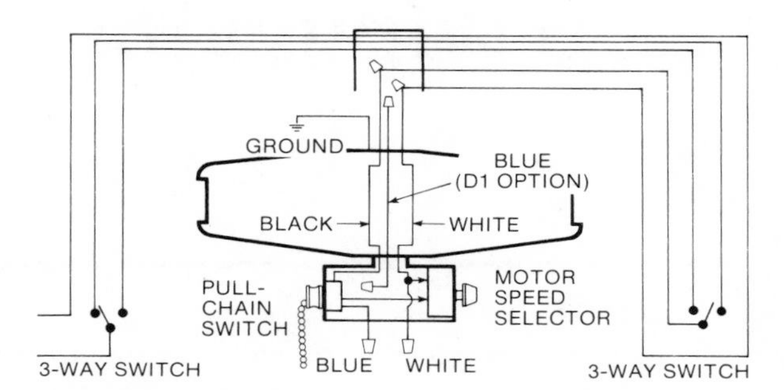

Figure 7-24

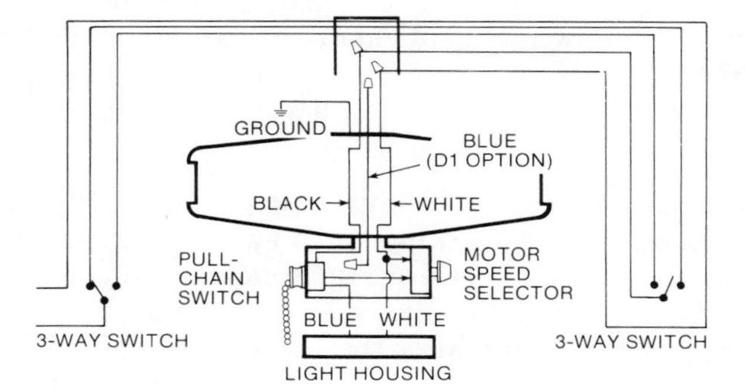

Figure 7-25

If new wiring is being installed, it is possible to have all controls on the wall instead of on the fan. A light dimmer can be used to control the lights, a wall control can be employed to control the fan, and a three-way wall switch (Leviton #5003, Hubbell #1203, or equivalent) can be used to control the fan blade's reversing action. This arrangement can be employed for most fan models. The only major fan wiring change is at the reverse switch. This only requires the cutting of reverse switch wires from the control and connecting them with wire nuts to the through wires which lead to the wall switch. Additional wiring in the fan should be done with 18 gauge wire.

APPENDIX

Other Energy Saving Tips

It is important to remember that a ceiling fan can be a great energy saving device only if a home is properly weatherized. Ceiling fans are designed to operate in closed environments, so unwanted drafts and other energy consuming faults can substantially reduce their efficiency. The following list of energy saving tips is provided to help you weatherize your home and increase the effectiveness of your ceiling fan. In other words, these tips plus your ceiling fan(s) will help save energy.

- **Weather Stripping/Caulking.** Look for cracks around doors, windows, and other openings such as those around pipes and ducts. Heat and air conditioning can escape at these points, so proper weather stripping and caulking are essential.
- **Thermostat.** In winter the thermostat should be set at 65° and should be set at least 5° lower when sleeping or away. In summer it should be set at 78° (for air conditioning). Alternate temperatures are recommended for homes with sick persons, elderly persons, or infants.
- **Heat-Producing Items.** During the months when the air conditioning is in operation, keep lamps, candles, and even television sets away from thermostats. The heat they create will make the air conditioner work harder, cooling more air than is necessary.
- **Water Heaters.** These appliances are the major energy users in a home. The thermostat should be set at a lower temperature and an insulating wrap applied to the water heater itself. Install water flow restrictors in showers and faucets. They cut hot water use without affecting family comfort. When removing an old water heater, choose an energy efficient model to replace it.

• **Repair Drips.** A leaking hot water faucet that can fill a tea cup in 10 minutes will waste 3,280 gallons of hot water a year.

• **Heating/Cooling System.** Filters for these systems should be cleaned or replaced as needed. Keep the outdoor portion of your air conditioner or heat pump clear of leaves, grass, or dirt accumulations. (Always disconnect electricity at circuit breaker or fuse box before cleaning.) Vents should be closed in unused rooms and pipes and ducts should be insulated in unheated spaces. Consider alternate devices such as ceiling fans to increase the efficiency of your present unit and choose an energy efficient model when replacing the system.

• **Radiator Tips.** For more efficiency, place a sheet of aluminum foil between the wall and the radiator. It will reflect the heat back into the room where it can be circulated more evenly by your fan. If you use decorative radiator covers, make sure they are not trapping and wasting precious heat.

• **Furnace Area Maintenance.** Keep the space all around your furnace clean. Dust, lint, and litter can cause operating problems as well as safety hazards.

• **Zone Heating.** If there are several thermostats in your home, energy can be saved by keeping the temperatures low in the rooms which are infrequently used. Also, close doors between heating zones.

• **Unused Rooms.** There is no need to heat or cool space that is not in use. Maintain only enough heat in these areas to avoid freezing the pipes.

• **Humidify in Winter.** Water vapor present in the air helps to reduce the cold sensation and makes life more comfortable at lower temperatures. This is a definite aid to ceiling fan usage because the air tends to "hold" the heat longer, allowing the fan to circulate it more evenly. A built-in humidifier or freestanding unit can be obtained to suit the home's arrangement. Set the operating level according to the manufacturer's recommendations.

• **Sunlight.** It is important to keep direct sunlight out in the summer and let it in during the winter. Drapes, shutters, awnings, glass with reflective film, and solar screens also help. According to the U.S. Department of Commerce, outdoor awnings, overhangs, or louvered sunscreens can reduce solar heat gain by as much as 80%.

• **Landscaping.** Properly placed trees, shrubs, vines, and other greenery near the walls of your house will keep the heat from escaping. Plant shade trees about 15′ to 20′ from the house on the western side. They help to stop the hot afternoon sun in summer and in winter they lose their leaves, letting the sunshine through to the house.

• **Appliances and Lighting.** Clothes dryers, washers, and dishwashers should be fully loaded when they are operated. Unnecessary lights should be turned off. If the lighting or appliances need replacing, energy efficient units should be used.

- **Drying Clothes Outdoors.** Even if you own a clothes dryer, hanging clothes outdoors to dry in warm seasons should be considered.
- **Closing Appliance Doors.** Family members should be instructed not to leave refrigerator or freezer doors open for long periods. Every extra second the door is left open increases the power needed to return the interior to its proper temperature.
- **Entertainment Equipment.** TV's, radios, record players, cassette decks, etc., should be turned off when not in use.
- **Better Lighting Sources.** When replacing home lighting, remember that fluorescent tubes produce more light for a given amount of energy consumed. The U.S. Department of Commerce also notes that extended service or "long life" light bulbs are actually less efficient than the ordinary variety.
- **Attic Insulation.** The attic should be checked to see if the recommended amount of insulation is present, including the attic door.
- **Floors and Foundation Walls.** These areas should also be checked. Adequate insulation must be present under floors, around the basement, in crawl spaces, and along foundation walls. Proper insulation aids ceiling fan operation by reducing unwanted drafts.
- **Windows and Doors.** Storm windows, doors, or double-paned glass helps to keep the heat and air conditioning on the inside where it belongs.
- **Exterior Walls.** Added insulation should be considered when remodeling or re-siding your house.
- **Seal up Cracks.** Stone, stucco, and brick exterior walls can develop energy wasting cracks. Repairs can be made with putty or a caulking compound.
- **Teach Children to Save.** A child is never too young to learn a few simple steps of energy conservation. Teach all family members to enter and leave the house quickly, in both winter and summer, without lingering in the doorway. Valuable heating and cooling energy escapes every time the door is opened. Remember, ceiling fans can help to conserve energy only if you help them. Unwanted drafts are the greatest energy thieves.
- **Wear a Sweater and Save.** Most energy "experts" suggest warm, loose clothing and sweaters to save energy and money in winter. They point out that when you regularly wear a sweater, the thermostat can be lowered by 3°, thereby saving as much as 10% on fuel bills. This factor, coupled with the air destratification capabilities of ceiling fans, can add up to real energy savings.